The Making of the

SEVERN RAILWAY TUNNEL

The Making of the

SEVERN RAILWAY TUNNEL

ROGER COWLES

ALAN SUTTON

1989

ALAN SUTTON PUBLISHING
BRUNSWICK ROAD · GLOUCESTER · UK

ALAN SUTTON PUBLISHING INC
WOLFEBORO · NEW HAMPSHIRE · USA

First Published 1989

British Library Cataloguing in Publication Data

Cowles, Roger
The making of the Severn Railway Tunnel.
1. England. Severn Estuary. Underwater railway
tunnels. Severn Tunnel, to 1985
I. Title
624.19409424

ISBN 0–86299–602–3

Library of Congress Cataloging in Publication Data
applied for

Typesettting and origination by
Alan Sutton Publishing Limited.
Printed in Great Britain.

Contents

Acknowledgements

My grateful thanks go to the following people, organizations and their staff for their help and support in the preparation of the book and for permission to publish copyright material and photographs: County Record Office, Gloucester; Miss Anne Rainsbury, Curator, Chepstow Museum; Science Museum; GWR Museum, Swindon; City of Bristol Museum and Art Gallery; Leicestershire Museums, Arts and Records Service; National Maritime Museum; Central Library, Bristol; Miss D.J. Bayley, Librarian, Institution of Civil Engineers; Siebe Gorman & Co. Ltd.; Thomas Nelson & Sons; British Rail; D.B. Barton; David & Charles; the Librarian, University of Bristol; *The Illustrated London News*.

My particular thanks also to: The staff of the Public Records Office, Kew; the late Thomas A. Walker for providing a remarkable record of the construction of the Severn Tunnel; two of his great-grandsons: John Harvey, who made many hitherto unpublished photographs available, and R.G.H. Walker, who read the manuscript and provided information, help and encouragement; Owen Harper for his research.

Introduction

The Severn Tunnel, completed in December 1886, took thirteen years to build. It is a rail tunnel 4¼ miles long connecting England and Wales below the River Severn, and is one of the most striking feats of civil engineering work to have been carried out during the latter part of the nineteenth century. It was a massive task; at the height of the work over 3,600 men were employed.

Between 1879 and 1886, a handful of buildings on the Welsh side of the river grew into Sudbrook village, built to house the workmen and their families. By the time the tunnel was completed the village consisted of well over a hundred houses, a school, a mission hall, a post office, coffee and reading rooms, a fully equipped infirmary and a fever hospital. There were also a large number of buildings associated with the works: offices, stores, workshops, pumping engine houses and boiler houses, and a large brickworks. But the real achievement was the construction of the tunnel itself. The following chapters chronicle the triumphs, frustrations and disappointments of thirteen eventful years.

1 *Inauspicious Beginnings*

In 1845, four years after his Great Western Railway from London to Bristol had been opened, Brunel devised a scheme for continuing the line to an existing ferry at New Passage, near Pilning, on the Gloucestershire shore of the Severn estuary. A huge pier would be built, extending into the estuary, with a similar pier at Portskewett on the Welsh side, thus affording a link with South Wales for passengers and freight.

Nothing was to become of Brunel's New Passage scheme until 1859, some fourteen years after its initial conception. By now Brunel's health was failing and he was anxious to obtain the services of a competent resident engineer to supervise work on the new line, which involved not only deep cuttings, but also a tunnel over 1,200 yd long just outside Bristol. He wrote to one of his former assistants, Charles Richardson:

> I want a man acquainted with tunnelling and who will, with a moderate amount of inspecting assistance look after the tunnel with his own eyes – for I am beginning to be sick of

Charles Richardson, designer of the Severn Tunnel
(Source: Thomas A. Walker, *The Severn Tunnel*)

inspectors who see nothing – and resident engineers who
reside at home and he must be one to whom salary is not
the principal object.

Brunel was only able to offer the modest salary of £300 a
year, rising to £450 a year when the full works commenced,
but offered in compensation:

> . . . the country immediately north of Bristol I should think
> a delightful one to live in – beautiful country – good society
> near Bristol & Clifton etc. – I can't vouch for any cricketing
> but should think it highly probable . . .

Richardson found the offer of cricket a little odd in view of
the fact that, some five years earlier, Brunel had admonished
him for playing too often. In any case, he thought the salary
unattractive. Knowing Richardson was unemployed, Brunel
wrote to him again:

> . . . if you desire on the other hand to go to work again . . .
> I think this is an excellent opportunity and again offer it to
> you provided you assure me that you enter upon it with
> pleasure and that a resumption of active life is an object to
> you . . .

Shortly before Brunel died at the age of fifty-three, a tired
and very ill man, Richardson accepted the post.

In 1833, when nineteen years old, Richardson had been
apprenticed to Brunel. His first experience of tunnelling was
on a scheme designed by Brunel's father, Marc, under the
Thames between Wapping and Rotherhithe. The younger
Brunel was resident engineer.

The only existing reliable, albeit slow, route to South

Wales at the time of Richardson's appointment was by rail via Swindon and Gloucester, along the Stroud valley, entailing the negotiation of heavy gradients and sharp curves. Some years earlier Brunel had proposed a branch off this line, crossing the Severn about 10 miles south-west of Gloucester, but local opposition was to thwart this proposal. Although the New Passage ferry scheme would reduce the distance to South Wales by 56 miles, it could never be wholly reliable with the vagaries of tides, and weather.

Under Richardson's charge, two massive piers, constructed of huge creosoted timbers, would jut out into the estuary. The pier at New Passage, on the English side, would be 1,635 ft long, with its counterpart on the Welsh side, at Black Rock near Portskewett, 708 ft long; each would be erected to a height of 50 ft above low water mark. Passengers would proceed in carriages to the pier head, where they would alight, proceed down some steps and board the ferry. At New Passage the piers were supported on timbers driven into the soft ground until they reached rock, at a depth which varied between 6 and 20 ft. The piers on the Welsh side were more problematical as the shore was rocky; cast-iron shoes had to be used at the base of the pier timbers, fixed to masonry foundations. It was while supervising this work that Richardson became fascinated by the notion of a tunnel under the Severn.

The tides of the Severn estuary rise rapidly, generating powerful swirling currents to catch out the unwary. These tides, the highest in Europe, the second highest in the world, are derived from the form of the estuary: the English and Welsh coasts funnel the water rapidly towards the mouth of the Wye, where a tidal rise of 50 ft can occur.

The River Severn effectively begins at Gloucester, where it

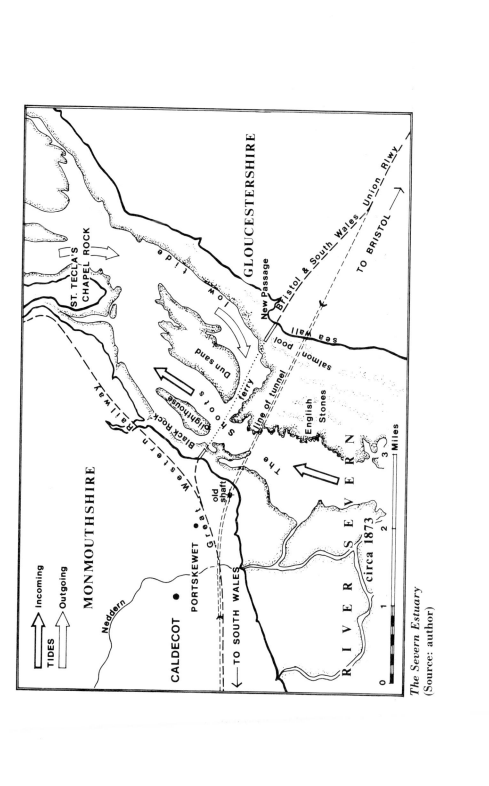

The Severn Estuary
(Source: author)

is only about 150 ft wide. Almost immediately it spreads into the tidal estuary consisting of sand at low tide and a broad channel of dirty water at high tide. Further down the estuary, the sand beds suddenly give way to rock, in an area called the English Stones. The junction between the sand beds and the rocks of the English Stones marks the line of the New Passage ferry crossing, where the water is over 40 ft deep at low water. In the vicinity of the ferry, Richardson observed that the English Stones were dry at low tide for a distance of about 2 miles across the estuary, the whole of the river then flowing rapidly through a deep rocky channel called the Shoots. He also noticed that on the incoming tide, water rushing up the Shoots was pressed against the Welsh shore. As the tide changed, the water was flung towards the English coast by the projecting St Tecla's Chapel Rock, leaving a sandbank called the Dun Sand in the middle of the estuary between the 'up' and 'down' currents. While the outgoing tide was high, the 'down' current flowed over the English Stones, but as the water level reduced, the rocks became a barrier, diverting the water back towards the Shoots. In so doing, it cut a channel through the sandbank, creating a deep water channel for the ferry. Vast quantities of sand were moved in the process.

A graphic illustration of the quantity and speed of movement of sand occurred while a survey of the ferry channel was being carried out. The survey boat ran aground on Dun Sand, so a man at the bow jumped out to push the boat off. He took two steps on the sand, intending a third to help him back into the boat. But his foot plunged into deep water; the sand was being moved so quickly that a vertical face had formed below the surface against the sandbank. Only by clutching tightly onto the side of the boat was he able to prevent himself from being swept away by the current.

The violence of the currents could also be seen as the excavations and masonry foundation work for the Black Rock pier bases were being carried out. The bases had to be built at low tide; as work stopped for the advancing tide, large quantities of gravel and stones, some bigger than a man's fist, were washed into the excavations. This material had to be removed before work could continue, a time-consuming and laborious process. Since all this work was taking place above low water level, it became obvious to Richardson that huge quantities of stones and gravel must run up and down the deeper channels. He deduced that the rock at the bottom of the river was hard enough to resist this scouring action, while any joints or fissures must be clogged with sand, gravel and mud, conditions which would allow the construction of a tunnel without fear of flooding from the river above.

Richardson presented his ideas to the directors of the Bristol and South Wales Union Railway, the company financing the work on the ferry; they were impressed with the notion of a tunnel and instructed him to proceed with further investigation of the estuary to consolidate his findings. He received particular encouragement from Mr Leonard Bruton, the secretary of the company.

During the subsequent survey work, the Severn again demonstrated its unpredictability. Three of Richardson's assistants, intent on taking some measurements on the English Stones, were deposited on the rocks by two boatmen. The boat should have waited, but instead the boatmen pulled out into the stream with the intention of rowing back later. In an instant the boat was carried away as the men desperately tried to resist the current. The rocks of the English Stones were rough, full of water-filled holes and covered in slippery seaweed, and the three assistants knew it would be impossible, with the rapidly advancing tide, to reach the shore in time. It was a harrowing experience as their shouts for help were drowned by the rush of the incoming tide. But they were lucky. The people on the shore, seeing that the boat did not arrive back at the appointed time, launched another boat to collect the men with minutes to spare.

By this time a shorter route to South Wales was rapidly becoming an economic necessity. In little more than twenty years, South Wales was to become a huge coalfield; in the Rhondda, twenty new pits would open between 1865 and 1875. By the 1880s coal production would reach over 20 million tons a year and the population of the area would grow faster than any other part of the United Kingdom. Much of the coal was taken to the Welsh ports, but transport inland to London and the south coast of England was still by the circuitous and time-consuming detour through Gloucester. The New Passage Ferry, which opened on a damp and dismal day in January 1864, was to afford no real alternative in this respect since in practice it provided little by way of freight facilities.

It is not surprising with such economic pressures that several schemes for crossing the Severn would be put forward as the railway companies vied with each other to tap the lucrative coal trade. The most popular solutions were crossings by bridge; tunnelling was seen as a risky and unpredictable process. It was a commonly held view that bridges were cheaper to build, maintain and widen. During this period a plethora of schemes was presented to parlia-

Opening of the New Passage Ferry
(Source: The Illustrated London News)

ment, plans showing the route of any new railway construction, together with a list of landowners affected, being
delivered in the form of a bill. Objections would be presented
and the proposals examined for financial security, the latter
normally taking the form of shares issued by the railway
companies. It was against this background that plans for the
Severn Tunnel were prepared following the necessary survey
work, and those plans deposited with parliament in 1863.

The most serious rival to the tunnel at this time was a
scheme produced by John Fowler and Hamilton Fulton
entitled 'The South Wales and Great Western Direct Railway', a project supported by the Great Western Railway. A
high-level viaduct 2¼ miles long, with modest gradients
suitable for goods trains, was proposed between Oldbury
and Chepstow. It would be 110 ft above high water level
with three openings, one of 600 ft (far greater than any other
bridge in the United Kingdom at that time) and two of
265 ft, across the main channel. The rest of the viaduct
would have over eighty other arches of various spans
between 150 and 90 ft; it would cost £1,800,000. All in all it
was a formidable project. But there was a great deal of
resistance to it by the merchants of Gloucester, who claimed
that the limited clearance beneath the bridge would seriously
affect shipping trade to the city. As a consequence of these
representations, the maximum height of the bridge was
raised to 120 ft, although this would still mean that the sailing
vessels would have to lower part of their rigging. It should be
borne in mind in this context that sailing vessels not only had
to contend with difficult currents and sandbanks in the
Severn, but they may also have had to tack from side to side,
making the negotiation of a bridge opening far more difficult
and hazardous than it might appear.

There were additional objections on engineering grounds, but 'Fowler's Line', as it came to be called, received parliamentary approval, whilst Richardson's scheme for the tunnel was turned down through lack of financial support.

Disappointed but undaunted, Richardson presented his idea to merchants, traders and others interested in improved rail links with South Wales, at a meeting in Bristol in 1865. The railway system had arrested Bristol's decline and it was agreed that better links with South Wales were vital to ensure the continued growth of prosperity in the city.

Richardson presented his proposals in an authoritative and confident manner. A bridge, he claimed, would be in danger of being struck by ships and there would be interference with navigation, exacerbated by the mists and fogs of the estuary. The tunnel would carry none of these risks. It would cost £750,000, a bridge nearly two and a half times that amount. He proposed that the capital for the tunnel be raised in 35,000 shares of £20 each.

While the Great Western Railway were, with some reluctance, backing Fowler's plan, the meeting resolved that the tunnel was the better scheme, and that the Great Western should support it. Richardson's pedigree obviously impressed the meeting: 25 years of tunnelling experience including Box and Thames tunnels, the latter constructed through mud and quicksand. If it was possible to tunnel beneath the Thames, the same was true of any river, Richardson reasoned. He dismissed criticism of the steep gradient through the tunnel on the ground that it was a small price to pay when the scheme cost a million pounds less than the bridge.

Richardson continued to strive for support from interested parties, this eventually culminating in another submission to parliament. Again he failed through lack of sufficient financial support. In the meantime, Fowler's Line was losing favour due to disagreements over working rates on the line, and had still not been started.

A proliferation of schemes for crossing the Severn arose in 1871; including the tunnel, no fewer than six with a total cost of £7,100,000 were to be brought before parliament. Three schemes sought to cross the Severn by bridge at Sharpness, one by high-level bridge from Tidenham to Almondsbury, one by bridge from Caldicot to Almondsbury, and Richardson's tunnel scheme, again revived. There was also another, proposed by Fulton, which envisaged a crossing under the river near Lydney, on a line similar to the three bridge schemes at Sharpness, but the concept did not progress very far.

Leonard Bruton, secretary of the Bristol and South Wales Union Railway which had been amalgamated with the Great Western in 1868, continued to give help and encouragement to Richardson. Together they addressed meetings at Cardiff and Newport Chambers of Commerce, but reservations were still expressed and Richardson decided to approach two eminent railway contractors, George Wyles and Thomas Brassey, to whom he explained his plans in detail. The spectre of the unknown still dogged his scheme, however; Brassey even told the Great Western directors that he would like to build the tunnel, but only if half a million pounds more were provided for contingencies.

Although Richardson was still unable to muster the necessary funds for his tunnel, the Great Western Railway directors had begun to show interest in the scheme. They considered that it might be an appropriate and practical proposition, but first they required Richardson to obtain the support of a distinguished engineer before going to parlia-

Sir John Hawkshaw, Chief Engineer
(Source: Walker, *The Severn Tunnel*)

ment with such a novel undertaking. He approached Thomas Harrison, chief engineer of the North Eastern Railway, but Harrison was not convinced; it only needed an unknown open fissure in the rock forming the bottom of the river to render the tunnel impracticable. Richardson's next approach was to John Hawkshaw, a highly respected engineer who, in his eighty years, was responsible not only for some of the most difficult engineering works, but also for a greater number of major projects than any other nineteenth-century engineer. He was to establish the practicability of a tunnel between England and France, a model upon which all subsequent channel projects would be based. When Richardson approached him about the Severn idea, Hawkshaw already had considerable experience in building tunnels. He carefully studied Richardson's proposals and after some deliberation concluded that the project was a viable one. At last Richardson had the support he needed. But the tunnel was not the only scheme seeking attention.

Of the five bridge concepts put forward in 1871, one serious rival to the tunnel was the plan put forward by William Low and George Thomas for a bridge from Caldicot to Almondsbury, virtually on the line of the proposed tunnel. The bridge would cross the navigable channel of the Shoots by a span of 700 ft (even greater than Fowler's Line), supported on two piers to be erected in the deep waters of the Shoots. The scheme was supported by John Fowler.

Richardson and Fowler were asked by the Great Western directors to prepare a joint report on the tunnel and the Caldicot–Almondsbury bridge:

Report by John Fowler and Charles Richardson to the
Directors of the Great Western Railway.

13th December 1871

Gentlemen,

We have carefully considered the question of the proposed
crossing of the River Severn near the New Passage by a
bridge and by a tunnel and we have compared the relative
cost and advantages of the two proposed works.

We are of opinion that in case of either of the works
being completed they may be assumed to be equal as
regards their efficiency for the purposes of a railway and
also equal as regards cost of maintenance.

We estimate the cost of the bridge and railway at
£900,000.

We have no substantial grounds for believing that the
tunnel could be constructed for a less amount, unless a
head-way were first driven and the ground proved to be
favourable.

Under these circumstances and considering the
contingencies of time and construction of the two works,
we are of the opinion that on the whole it will be desirable
for the Board to adopt the bridge in preference to the
tunnel.

We are, gentlemen,
Your obedient servants,

(signed) John Fowler
       Charles Richardson

On the same date, William Low wrote to the Chairman of the Great Western Railway, explaining the details of the bridge and adding: 'I hope early in January (1872) to give you incontestible proofs of the impracticability of the *tunnel scheme* and equally incontestible proof of the practicability of the *bridge scheme*. . . .'

Low wrote again on 1 January:

> . . . we beg to state that we consider we have now obtained sufficient data to prove to the Chairman the utter impracticability of constructing the proposed tunnel . . . of course a simple opinion expressed by us relative to the difficulties to be overcome in the construction of this work is apt to be considered prejudiced on account of our having a bridge scheme, and it is thought strange that we should condemn a four mile tunnel whilst we advocate a 22 mile tunnel across the Straits of Dover. Our answer is that the *stratification* is quite different. The Straits of Dover can only be practically crossed at one place. Some people imagine that a tunnel can be made anywhere. In condemning the tunnel under the Severn, we do so as practical mining engineers which we can demonstrate from the facts which we have obtained as clearly as a problem in Euclid. We feel convinced that when we lay the facts before Mr Hawkshaw that he will abandon the work rather than risking his reputation by advocating a work that must be a perfect failure . . . we should be glad of an opportunity to meet the Great Western Directors named in our Bill so as to explain to them fully the estimate and practicability of the Severn Bridge scheme, and to expose the absurdity of the proposed tunnel scheme as laid out in the Parliamentary plans deposited by Mr Richardson. . . .

In the face of such mounting criticism, and bearing in mind the conclusions of the report of 13 December, it seems that

winds. After some deliberation he came up with the figure of
8 ft. A big spring tide, if it occurred in calm weather, would
flood the lands next to the estuary to a depth of over 3 ft and,
if a gale and a high spring tide should coincide, the water
could reach a depth of 11 ft or more. Allowing for a margin
of safety, Richardson reasoned that the sea banks around the
top of the cutting should be 16 ft high.

In seeking further facts to prove his hypothesis, Richardson found an account of a flood in the seventeenth
century, with illustrations of cattle swimming among trees
and haystacks floating away, but no facts about water depths
were given. He sought further evidence. Thinking that
churches in the lowland areas might bear a record of floods,
he scoured the locality and found at Peterstone, on the Welsh
side of the river, a church with a lead plug set into the wall to
mark the height of a big flood. Peterstone had been a small
port, with at one time more shipping than Newport; the
great storm and tide destroyed everything except the church
tower and the strong wall of a warehouse.

An even more graphic account was found in the church of
Kingston Seymour, a village over 1½ miles from the banks of
the estuary. On a black board, printed in gold letters, he read:

> January 20th, 1606, and 4th year of James 1st. An
> inundation of sea water, by overflowing and breaking down
> the sea banks, happened in this parish of Kingston Seamore,
> and many others adjoining, by reason whereof many
> persons were drowned, and much cattle and goods were
> lost. The water in the church was five feet high, and the
> greatest part lay on the ground about ten days.
>
> (signed) William Bower.

(Note: Kingston *Sea*more is an old spelling)

On another black board in the same church:

> On November 27th, 1702, a flood occurred, destroying the
> sea bank, drowning much cattle, and destroying hayricks,
> etc.

Significantly, the biggest tides never occur in January or
November. A storm coinciding with a very big spring tide
would be so rare that it would occur on average perhaps once
every hundred years. Daniel Gooch was later to remark that
he thought the sea banks Richardson planned around the
cuttings would hardly be necessary under these circumstances; events were to prove otherwise.

2 | *Starting the Work*

Detailed survey completed, it was now time to start the construction work, with Richardson as Chief Engineer and John Hawkshaw as Consulting Engineer. The directors had agreed that the ground under the Shoots be tested first and Richardson's plan was to sink a circular shaft down through the rocks exposed at low water at the edge of the Shoots; from the bottom of this shaft a small tunnel or heading would be carried below the deep water channel. Obviously at high tide the shaft would fill with water, so a strong hollow watertight tower would first need to be constructed on the rocks to a height well above the highest tides; the shaft could then be sunk inside the tower irrespective of the water level outside. But there was a great deal of opposition to the tower on the grounds that it would be dangerous to shipping. Richardson regarded this opposition as somewhat captious bearing in mind the earlier approval of numerous bridge piers across the estuary for 'Fowler's Line'. He was prompted to comment at the time that the authorities would 'object to anything new, whether good or bad'.

As a result of the objections, the shaft was begun on the

shore instead, about half a mile from the Shoots, in the small agricultural parish of Portskewett (total population 260), on 22 March 1873. No buildings were in existence at the site of the shaft, the nearest being a farmhouse known as Sudbrook or Southbrook farm, just under half a mile away. Slightly further away, along the river bank, was the Black Rock Hotel, a resting place for travellers using the New Passage Ferry. The Great Western Railway purchased a small parcel of land near the location of the shaft on which they built six cottages and an office for the men who would be working there.

The shaft, 15 ft in diameter after lining with brickwork and about 200 ft deep, would form a permanent pumping station; rainwater would of course run into the tunnel from the cuttings at either end, to the lowest point below the Shoots, and pumps would be necessary to control this water. Another consideration, with steam trains producing fumes and smoke in the tunnel, was some form of forced ventilation. This work would be carried out by a huge fan mounted over the top of a shaft leading to the tunnel; it would suck air up the shaft, the foul air being replaced by fresh air entering each tunnel mouth. Having to move the shaft on to the shore meant that the fan would no longer be near the middle of the tunnel, thus making the ventilation of the longer section of the tunnel that much more difficult. This problem was to occupy Richardson for some time.

The Great Western directors placed a contract with William Dennis and Benjamin Perkins of Bristol for carrying out the sinking of the shaft. The railway company would provide a single line of track from Portskewett station to the shaft and would supply all the bricks, lime, sand and cement. A winding engine with a lift cage in the shaft would transport six men at a time or lift a skip of excavated material to the surface. A substantial beam engine and pump would be available to clear any water encountered in the shaft during its construction. Coal and water would be needed for fuelling the steam engines to power the machinery, and a large shed would be erected over the top of the shaft to protect it from the weather. Substantial quantities of heavy timber would be needed to provide temporary support to the sides of the shaft until the brick lining was completed. A blacksmith's shop, fitting shop and stores for blasting powder (kept in a separate shed) and other items would also be necessary. The contractor would be required to work twenty-four hours a day.

By August 1873, the shaft was about 60 ft deep, but progress had not been without incident. At a depth of 45 ft a strong spring was met with, compounded a few feet further down by a second, much larger, spring which completely overwhelmed the existing pumping power and brought the work to a stop. It was not until a much larger pump and spare had been obtained that the task could continue.

'Fowler's Line' was now defunct, the Great Western Railway and the promoters being unable to agree working rates over the proposed line, and finance was not forthcoming. On the other hand, discussion was still continuing between the Great Western Railway directors and the Severn Bridge Railway Company concerning a contribution by the former to the cost of the bridge across the Severn at Sharpness. The bridge would connect the Great Western Railway on the western side of the river with the Midland Railway on the eastern side, thus linking the latter with collieries and ironworks of the Forest of Dean and making the Great Western route from London to South Wales much shorter. There would be virtually the same reduction in distance provided by the tunnel, but the bridge would have the advantage of far less severe gradients to negotiate. If both bridge and tunnel were completed, the Severn Bridge Railway directors were of the opinion that mineral traffic across the river could be carried more cheaply by the bridge. The Severn Bridge Railway Company were anxious to establish an amicable working arrangement with the Midland and the Great Western, but the Great Western were less than enthusiastic, due partly to their commitment to the tunnel and partly to the proposed terms of the Midland Railway involvement with the bridge project.

In March 1874, Richardson wrote to Gooch describing a tunnelling machine which he thought would greatly simplify the construction of the tunnel. The machine, mounted on rails, had large revolving cutters at one end that would cut a clean circular hole, the diameter of the tunnel, through the rock as the machine slowly advanced. It would only be necessary to provide a lining of brickwork. The work would be carried out much more quickly and a considerable amount of hand labour would be eliminated since debris would be automatically loaded into wagons at the rear of the machine. The need for blasting, with its associated risks, would be overcome.

Hawkshaw, however, was not impressed with Richardson's proposal; he wrote to Gooch pointing out that the machine would be satisfactory in rock, but the shales and clays that would be met with in the Severn Tunnel works would simply clog the cutters. He advocated the traditional method of hand labour, with rock drills and blasting.

In August 1874 the secretary of the Great Western Railway sent a letter to the Severn Bridge Railway Company:

You will remember that previously to the Bill for the line
being brought before the Committee of the House of
Commons, Sir Daniel Gooch was so desirous of avoiding
the necessity of opposing the scheme that he came to an
arrangement with you . . . whereby he undertook to
recommend his colleagues and the shareholders to subscribe
under certain conditions towards the undertaking . . . the
course taken by the Chairman must have satisfied you that
he desired to avoid as far as possible any hostility to the
scheme. The whole subject has again received the best
consideration of my Board, but the circumstances under
which the Chairman originally assented to subscribe are
materially changed and I am desired to inform you that the
Directors do not now consider it desirable to exercise the
option of subscribing towards the undertaking. . .

Although discussions would continue on the subject of the
Severn Bridge, the Great Western Railway now seemed fully
committed to the tunnel.

After some difficulty with rock and water, the bottom of
the shaft on the shore was reached in December 1874. At a
depth of 200 ft the heading was started in the direction of the
Shoots. The heading would be 7 ft square and would rise
gently beneath the Shoots to the lowest point of the tunnel. It
would, when the tunnel was completed, form a permanent
drain; water would be pumped from the bottom of the shaft
by a pumping station.

Headings are used in tunnelling not only to test the
ground, but also to set out an accurate line for building the
main tunnel. A heading may pass through solid rock or
through a whole range of materials, some of which could be
soft and loose. In the case of the former, it may only be
necessary to provide occasional timbers to support the roof,
but in the case of the latter, horizontal and vertical timber

supporting members may be required, with flat boards in between to retain the loose material.

Initially work was carried out by hand drilling the rock and blasting, but even working day and night in twelve-hour shifts only 4 yd a week could be achieved. At the end of January, air-driven drills had been introduced, fed from a wrought-iron pressure vessel on the surface by wrought-iron pipes which carried the compressed air to the drills at the working face. This innovation was not popular with the men who felt that the traditional methods were better, but a temporary breakdown in the air pump served to convince them when they had to return to hand drilling for a time.

Dynamite was used instead of the older blasting powder, and proved to be much more effective. Holes would be drilled in the face and packed with explosive. Although blasting powder broke up the rock, it produced big pieces which had to be broken up with sledge-hammers before they could be loaded into the trolleys to be taken away; the powder also produced large quantities of smoke. On the other hand, dynamite was much more powerful, blowing the rock away cleanly into small shovel-sized pieces for the full depth of the drill hole, and thus gaining a few vital inches with every set of charges.

The men, working in three eight-hour shifts at this stage, and by using the compressed air drills and dynamite, were progressing at the rate of 14–18 yd per week. Working conditions in the heading were far from pleasant; in addition to the water coming into the works, the men had to contend with heat from the drills and their own exertions, while constantly having to breathe the toxic fumes from the dynamite. The air from the drills helped to ventilate the heading for a time, but after about 200 yd the conditions became intolerable. In May 1875 Richardson ordered some 12-in diameter galvanized pipes which were laid along the heading and connected to a large steam-powered extract fan on the surface; this facility improved the working conditions considerably.

In June 1875, more than two years after starting the work, all that had been done was the sinking of a shaft and just over two hundred yards of heading. This date also marked the start of the construction of the Severn Bridge at Sharpness. It was to be nearly 1,400 yd long, carrying the railway 70 ft above high water on twenty-one spans supported on huge cast-iron cylinders filled with concrete or brickwork. In addition there would be a swing bridge, powered by steam engines, over the Gloucester and Berkeley Ship Canal at the eastern end, thus minimizing inconvenience to shipping. The bridge would reduce the distance between South Wales and Bristol by 30 miles, and a new outlet for the iron ore and coal of the Forest of Dean would have been secured.

The end of July 1875 saw about 300 yards of heading under the river completed, but the going was getting more difficult. Although the rock was sound and hard, there were open joints which produced a good deal of water, making the working conditions very difficult and prompting the men to ask for more money. Great reliance was placed upon the pumps to keep the heading clear of water, but at the end of October one of the two pumps failed, bringing the work to a standstill. This was to happen on two or three occasions; in one instance a drill passed into a water-filled joint causing water to shoot 20 ft along the heading, completely overwhelming the pumps. Clearly this must have been a frightening experience for the men, working in hot, wet conditions by flickering lamplight deep below the Severn, at any moment expecting the river to break in. But the water was fresh in every case and originated from fresh water springs contained in the rock.

In anticipation of further problems, Richardson ordered a heavy wall, 6 ft thick, to be built across the heading about 340 yd from the shaft. The wall would be fitted with a thick iron door 5 ft by 3 ft; two cast-iron pipes would be built into the wall to control the water, one fitted with a large valve, the other with a flap. In the event that a flood should occur, the door and valve would be closed, sealing off the heading and enabling the pumps to bring the situation under control.

In February 1877, Richardson wrote to the Great Western directors in optimistic mood:

> The heading, which six months ago had just arrived at the Shoots, has been carried under the whole of the deep water under that channel. It has, along the entire distance, passed through compact Pennant rock and has been almost free from water, thus bearing out completely the favourable conclusions then arrived at as to the perfect success and practicability of the work. Plans, drawings and specifications are now being prepared for letting the work (for building the main tunnel) by contract.

Richardson originally intended to sink a series of shafts on the line of the tunnel about 1,000 to 1,500 yd apart across the estuary; this would mean that three shafts would be built on the rocks that were uncovered at low tide, one adjacent to the Shoots on the Welsh side, one by the Salmon Pool and one on the English Stones. The shaft by the Shoots had already been thwarted on navigational grounds, but the other two were still planned. In each case a tower would be built 18 ft in diameter and about 40 ft high, with w.lls 3 ft thick, the whole to be built at low tide. The shaft would then be sunk inside the tower, with materials being ferried out by barge from the shore, where a branch railway line would be built to serve the works. A 20 ft-thick layer of debris would be tipped around the base of the tower to make it safe from collision, and a landing stage would be constructed for the barges. Support for steam-driven winding engines would be required to raise and lower material and equipment in the shaft.

By August 1877, the heading under the river was nearly a mile long. A second shaft had been started adjacent to the original, to accommodate the pumps to drain the tunnel. This shaft would be 18 ft in diameter compared with the 15 ft of the original, or 'Old Shaft' as it came to be known, and would give far more space for the pumps and equipment. The new shaft, which would be connected to the main heading by a short linking heading, would be lined with curved iron plates about 7 ft by 4 ft, bolted to one another.

The Great Western directors decided at this stage to publish advertisements asking for tenders for the whole of the tunnel works; three were received:

Rowland Brotherhood (Bristol)	£ 987,372	10*s.*	0*d.*
Thomas A. Walker (London)	£1,032,531	15*s.*	9*d.*
William Webster (London)	£1,350,000	0*s.*	0*d.*

Richardson was bitterly disappointed; these figures were substantially higher than his estimates, but reflected the apprehension of the contractors in carrying out an under-taking of this magnitude, where so much remained unknown.

Hawkshaw, now Sir John, advised the directors to accept

the tender of Thomas Walker, who had worked under him on the continuation of Brunel's original Thames tunnel under the London docks. That construction was carried out under very difficult circumstances and this, together with other work carried out on the London Underground, could prove to be invaluable experience to Walker in building the Severn Tunnel. Richardson was not impressed; on 24 August 1877 he wrote to Sir Daniel Gooch:

> In this very important crisis in the affairs of the Severn Tunnel I . . . write to you in confidence . . . what I think about the affairs for I differ in my opinion from Sir John on several important points . . . I have always prided myself upon making a fair working estimate and I think I have done so in this sense at the time it was made. I do not at all like to see my work made to cost so much more than my estimate or than I think it ought to cost. I do not perceive the advantage to us of tying ourselves for better or for worse to a man (Walker) who cannot on his part give a sufficient guarantee for the execution of the work . . . I should greatly fear besides that if the contract is let to Walker it will certainly cost all the contract sum. Sir John's work is, in my estimation, costly, in excess of any useful purpose, but under this contract what power should I or anyone else have to reduce the work to what I think fair proportions with Sir John himself as final arbitrator on points in dispute, Sir John recollect with his large ideas of the work and his own contractor accustomed to carrying out these ideas of excessively heavy work, a sort of work which pays a contractor well. . . . Walker may have been a useful man to Sir John, who appears to have taken a great fancy to him but . . . as a contractor . . . he certainly comes from a bad school . . . I know nothing of him myself however except that he came down here during my absence and blustered greatly about himself and Sir John. The

bridges and culvert drawings are made greatly more costly than I think necessary. I gave Sir John sketches of the different bridges for the drawings to be made from, but he put them aside as lighter than his usual work and either modified them or substituted his own entirely . . . I of course intended if the contract had been let to have introduced my own drawing again, but suppose the contractor had preferred Sir John's drawing . . . I should have had to look on whilst £3000 was, so far as my judgement was concerned, completely thrown away on one bridge . . . if Walker has the contract I much fear that I shall be powerless to control these things. . . .

The Great Western directors discussed at great length the question of how to proceed and, perhaps influenced by Richardson's letter, accepted his advice that the best approach would now be to drive a heading for the full length of the tunnel. Fresh tenders would then be invited on the basis that the ground had been proved and a lot of the uncertainty eliminated; more realistic prices for the work should then be received.

Richardson's plans for the towers in the estuary had also been foiled by the navigation authorities; no tipping would be allowed around the towers and the cost of transporting the material by barge would be prohibitive. This meant that the tunnel would have to be driven from shafts on each shore.

Two small contracts for driving the headings were made: one was with Oliver Norris of New Passage for sinking a shaft (the 'Sea Wall' shaft) on the Gloucestershire side of the river, and driving headings east and west; the other with Rowland Brotherhood of Bristol for sinking two further shafts (the 'Marsh Shaft' and 'Hill Shaft') on the line of the tunnel on the Monmouthshire side, with headings similarly east and west. The Great Western would continue the heading under the river themselves. It was later agreed that Oliver Norris would also drive a second heading from the Old Shaft east and west; this heading would be some 40 ft above the drainage heading driven earlier. Eventually all the headings would join together to link both sides of the river.

The new shaft referred to earlier was soon to be completed and lined with the curved iron plates for its full depth apart from about 12 ft of brickwork right at the bottom, which carried girders for the pumps. A small iron door, 2 ft square, was built into one of the iron plates lining the shaft to give access to the small heading linking the shaft to the original drainage heading. It became known as the 'Iron Shaft'.

Abandoning the idea of shafts in the estuary meant that the headings would have to be driven from shafts nearly 2½ miles apart, placing a premium on accuracy; even a small error over this distance might mean the headings from each side of the river missing one another entirely. The usual way of setting the line of the tunnel would be by using a plumb-line consisting of a wire with a substantial weight at the end, which would be suspended from the top of the shaft down to the heading below. If two such plumb-lines were used, suspended on opposite sides of the shaft, then by lining the two wires up at the surface with a distant marker on the line of the tunnel, because the wires would be truly vertical, the line could be transferred to the heading below. In the case of the Old Shaft, the wires were 200 ft long and each plumb-line swung slowly, like a pendulum. To reduce this effect the weights at the ends of the wires were submerged in water to steady them. Even so, the plumb-lines swung slowly from side to side, taking nearly eight seconds each way. In addition there was a vibration set up in the wires due

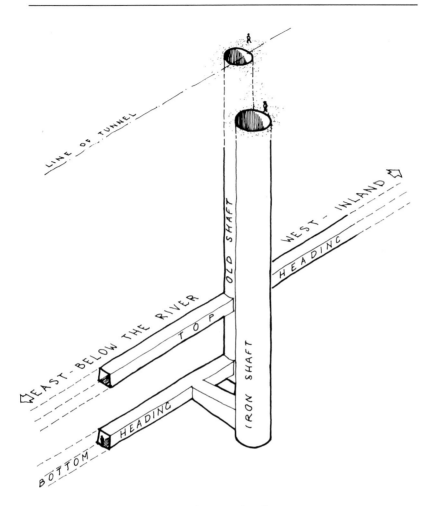

Old Shaft, Iron Shaft and headings in October 1879
(Source: author)

to the operation of the big water pump. This state of affairs prompted Richardson, in a contemporary report, to comment: '. . . it appears to the eye to be steady; but . . . first one and then the other appears to leave the line, and you may, as the writer did, spend an hour in vain trying to fix them, until your handkerchief is wet through with mopping up your tears, but you are never sure of accuracy. . . .' A better method had to be found.

A robust telescope was obtained, fixed in a special mounting at the top of the shaft, which enabled the instrument to line up with a flagstaff on the other side of the river, and then to be tilted vertically to look down the shaft at a wire travelling along the heading. With one end of the wire fixed to the far wall of the shaft at the bottom, the other end, some 250 ft along the heading, could be adjusted until the section of wire visible at the bottom of the shaft was exactly in line with the view through the telescope from the top. This had to be done several times to eliminate error, which was found to be a divergence from an accurate line of 2 ft in a mile, an unimportant amount normally, but with the distances involved in this case, clearly much more significant.

Sir Daniel Gooch made regular visits to the works, as entries in his diary indicate, but he was disappointed with progress:

> May 1st 1879 – I went to the Severn Tunnel and spent the day there, going up to the face of the heading. All going on well, but very slow. The day was fine with some showers. This is a very anxious job for me. Richardson, the engineer, has no go in him and does not move without consulting me, making me almost the engineer.

In the main heading under the river, at a distance of about

1¼ miles from the Old Shaft, a peculiar rock was encountered. This red sandstone was very hard to drill and, when blasted, the dynamite only blew out a round hole, but blew the rock into powder. When this material was put into iron skips and taken on rails to the bottom of the shaft, it was shaken down to such an extent that the water rose to the surface, and the sandy material in the skip was wedged in like concrete. On reaching the surface, it had to be broken out with pickaxes. Richardson had come across this rock once before in Wiltshire; if a hole was dug in it, the material removed would be inadequate to refill the hole, and extra would have to be brought from elsewhere to complete the filling. After placing, it set almost like mortar. On 5 September 1879, after about 50 yd of heading had been driven through this obstinate and frustrating rock, one of the men, operating a compressed air-driven drill, struck an open joint filled with water under pressure. As the drill was withdrawn a jet of water shot out of the hole, hitting the onlooking foreman with such a force he was knocked down and the jet flew 50 ft along the heading.

The incident caused great alarm. Water was pouring into the workings at a rate of 25,000 gallons an hour, placing a premium on the available pumping power. But again the water was fresh, and slowly dwindled to a moderate sized spring; fears of the river breaking in were unfounded.

3 The Great Spring

On 16 October, spirits were high. There were less than 140 yd to go between the east and west headings; once joined it would be possible to walk from one side of the river to the other. Sir Daniel Gooch had been invited to attend the opening ceremony of the Severn Railway Bridge the following day; he was looking forward to announcing the progress on the tunnel, and to issuing an invitation to his hosts to walk through the full length of the completed river heading. But as Oliver Norris's men toiled westwards along the top heading inland, disaster struck. A huge body of water was tapped which poured into the tunnel workings in such quantity that within 24 hours all the headings were flooded and the Old Shaft was filled to the level of the river. The existing pump installations were totally inadequate to deal with this catastrophe. The men struggled in vain to dam the heading, but the sheer mass of water made it impossible. Many lives would have been lost if the men working in the long heading below had not been changing shifts. When they retreated to the Old Shaft, they were met with a roaring torrent of icy water from the upper heading 40 ft above them. The only ping the flow of water into the Old Shaft. Two massive timber shields would be lowered down the shaft to cover the entrances to the two top headings and wedged tightly in position, a difficult proposition in view of the fact that the mouth of each heading was under 140 ft of water. After obtaining the approval of Sir John Hawkshaw, he put his plan into action on 6 January 1880. If it worked, and the Great Spring was held back, the water running down the lower heading from the springs under the river could easily be coped with by the existing pumping power.

The shields were of oak, about 12 ft by 11 ft, each weighing over 3 tons and curved to fit the interior of the shaft. The outer faces of the shields were padded with soft material soaked in tar to give a good seal against the brickwork.

Walker enlisted divers to carry out the work. Equipped with heavy diving suits, and with their heavy metal helmets fed by compressed air from the surface, they would descend to the level of the headings to guide the shields into position by signals to the men above. Oak struts would then be wedged between the two shields to hold them in position. Underwater lighting was not available; the work would have to be accomplished in complete darkness. The pumps were started to lower the water level in the shaft as much as possible to reduce the pressure on the divers; in their heavy suits, at a depth of 140 ft, strenuous physical exertion would be impossible. But the pumps kept breaking down, and then it was discovered that the small section of brickwork at the bottom of the Iron Shaft had been built so badly that the water being pumped out was being replaced at almost the same rate by leakage through the brickwork. The shields were in position, but on 24 January one of the divers found

Two of the shafts
(Source: John Harvey)

the shield sealing the western heading defective. Courageous attempts were made by the divers to seal the leaks, but more pump failures forced Walker to abandon his plan until the new engines and pumps were fixed. In one attempt to repair a broken pump, a diver was sucked with great force against the inlet of one of the working pumps, requiring the combined efforts of three strong men at the surface to haul him away by the rope around his waist.

On 9 March 1880, Sir John Hawkshaw wrote to the secretary of the Great Western Railway:

> In my report of 2nd December last I referred to the risk attending the construction of the tunnel under the Shoots. Since that time I have had under consideration the practicability of reducing the amount of that risk and now submit my views to the Board. This risk will be minimised if the level of the rails beneath the Severn were depressed, and I now recommend that this be done to an extent not exceeding fifteen feet. Lowering the level of the rails fifteen feet would increase the depth of the ground over the tunnel at the Shoots from 29 feet to about 44 feet and at the Salmon Pool from 15 feet to about 30 feet. The gradient under the Shoots on the Bristol side of the Severn will not be altered. The gradient on the Monmouthshire side, which is with the load, will be 1 in 90. The increased cost of the works by the alteration will not exceed £50,000. . .the additional cost will consist mainly in increased earthwork, lowering the shafts, lengthening the pumps, and the purchase of additional land. . . .

The directors agreed to Hawkshaw's proposal, but Richardson was altogether against the idea. He lodged his objections with the Board on 21 April 1880:

I wish it to be understood that the paper I wrote to you in indication of my position as having projected and advised the construction of the tunnel still expresses my confident opinion. The main reason against lowering the gradient is of course the increased cost, and if there is any doubt about the safety of the old lines it would be wise to lower them as proposed. But knowing the strata as I do, I have myself no doubt. . . .

Richardson suggested driving another heading about 300 yd long underneath the Shoots, 20 ft above the existing heading, to further prove the ground; this work would only take twenty weeks. But he was again overruled. Walker also intimated that the greatest problem was not under the Shoots, but inland, in the direction of the Great Spring.

In the meantime, further shafts had been commenced; one 18 ft in diameter adjacent to the Old and Iron shafts, and two further shafts to the west, intended to deal with the Great Spring, located at a point called 'Five Miles Four Chains'. This odd designation stems from the tradition in railway work of measuring distances from the starting point of a particular contract to the point under consideration. In this case, the contract was deemed to commence in Gloucestershire, about 2½ miles from the shore. The two new shafts, one for winding (equipped with a cage for men and materials), the other for pumping, would therefore be located 5 miles 4 chains from this starting point, a chain being 22 yd. In addition, a second shaft would be sunk on the Gloucestershire side of the river for pumping purposes, the original shaft reverting to the role of winding shaft.

Work was now proceeding at quite a pace on both sides of the river, and more labour was required. Walker decided to lease a plot of land near the Old and Iron shafts on which to build some cottages for the men. He had experimented successfully with making bricks from the clays and marls in the area and as a consequence decided to build a large brickyard with a substantial drying shed near the new shafts at Five Miles Four Chains. During the sinking of these two shafts, Walker noticed that the material being brought up from below bore a strong resemblance to the type being used by the Cattybrook Brickworks, just north of Bristol, in the manufacture of vitrified bricks. These bricks had a high strength and were made from crushed shale, a rock similar to slate but softer, which was moulded into shape and then heated to a high temperature in a kiln or oven. The brick lining to the tunnel would have to resist enormous pressures underground, requiring very high strength bricks of this type. Walker decided to substantially increase his existing brick-making capacity by erecting eight massive Staffordshire kilns, a huge crushing mill and a drying shed 100 ft by 150 ft.

The battle continued to free the headings and shafts of water, with the divers fully employed in clearing obstructions and keeping the pumps active. Increased pumping power was now available in the Iron Pit and, by mid-afternoon on 2 July 1880, the water level had dropped almost to the bottom of the Iron Shaft. But suddenly and without warning a cast-iron pump at the bottom of the shaft burst apart. This was a terrifying experience; the pump was over 3 ft in diameter and several feet long, connected to the surface by large wrought-iron pipes. A huge 18-in chunk of the pump flew out, narrowly missing one of the men at the bottom of the pit. Almost immediately the beam of the engine above, weighing nearly 23 tons, losing the resistance of the pump, crashed onto a safety stop. Before the engine could be halted, the beam struck the stop again with another thunderous blow.

It was pointless expecting the remaining pumping capacity to cope with the water. In a few hours the works had returned to the state they were in seven months earlier; full of water to the level of the tide.

The incident was investigated by Sir John Hawkshaw. The pump and pipework connecting it to the surface would have to be taken out of the shaft. This exercise took nearly two weeks; first the pump rods of heavy timber 45 ft long and fitted with iron mountings, and then 9-ft lengths of wrought-iron pipe over 3 ft in diameter had to be removed one at a time from the 200 ft deep shaft. It was the morning of 14 October 1880 before all the necessary parts were obtained and the pumps made ready for action again. By the beginning of November, the water in the workings had been reduced to a level about 160 ft below the surface, leaving a depth of about 40 ft at the bottom of the shaft.

There was still a fair quantity of spring water coming into the workings from the heading under the river. The heavy wall, 6 ft thick, which Richardson had built across the heading some years previously was not carrying out its designed function; the heavy iron door and the two valves in the wall had been left open by the men in the panic to get out of the workings. In an effort to reduce the flow of water from this source, Walker resolved to close the door and valves, thus enabling him to concentrate on the Great Spring. This would not be easy; the wall lay 40 ft below the surface and about 1,000 ft from the bottom of the Old Shaft. He planned to use divers for the work. The leading diver would descend the shaft, then walk 1,000 ft along the heading to the wall, trailing his air hose behind him. He would climb through the

Alexander Lambert, diver (in bowler hat), photographed at a diving exhibition
(Source: Siebe Gorman and Company Limited)

door opening, close the flap over the end of one of the pipes, pull up the rails used by the skips, close the door, close the valve on the other pipe and return to the shaft. The whole operation would have to be carried out in total darkness. Few divers would have relished the prospect of implementing Walker's plan.

Walker intended to employ Alexander Lambert as leading diver. Lambert – 'a fair haired man of few words, but of great courage' as Charles Richardson later described him – was already a diver of some considerable standing and the leader of a team from the famous diving firm of Siebe Gorman and Company. In his early forties, Lambert was a big man, barely 5 ft 8 in tall, but with a massive chest and powerful arms and legs. To entertain youngsters he would grip the back of a heavy chair with his teeth and hoist it clean over his head. He was a cheerful character with a soft voice and a keen sense of humour. Wearing 20 lb diving boots, a 40 lb breast plate and a metal helmet of 60 lb, he would need all his strength to haul his air hose and lines along 1,000 ft of flooded heading. Two other divers would assist, one at the bottom of the shaft to guide the hose, the second about 500 ft along the heading to feed it to Lambert.

On 3 November 1880, Lambert descended the shaft to make his attempt. Clutching a short iron bar he groped his way in complete darkness along a heading that he had never seen, stumbling over debris, tools and equipment left behind in the panic when the Great Spring broke in. As he advanced further into the heading he had to stoop to avoid the mass of supporting timbers overhead. His air pipe floated hard against the roof, making progress more and more difficult. Eventually, when only about 200 ft from the door, Lambert was forced to concede defeat. But his return to the shaft proved to be even more hazardous; as he retraced his steps, the air pipe on which his life depended had become curled up in kinks and coils about the supporting timbers of the heading. Feeling around in total darkness he disentangled and gathered up the coils of pipe, and hauled them over the obstacles he had negotiated earlier. All the time the coils kept slipping from his grasp. He eventually arrived back at the shaft, bitterly disappointed at his failure. Richardson was later to write: 'It was astonishing that his courage could have sustained him through such a trial; for . . . if ever his heart had failed him, he would not have come out alive.'

A few years before Lambert's exploit, Henry Fleuss, a thin lively Wiltshireman in his twenties and an officer in the merchant marine, started making and experimenting with self-contained underwater breathing apparatus. In 1879, he demonstrated his apparatus to the public by submerging himself in a few feet of water contained in a tank at the Old Polytechnic in Regent Street, London, for periods of about an hour. It consisted of a stiffened, watertight, rubber-proofed fabric mask fitted over the face, connected by two breathing tubes to a flexible bag worn on the diver's back. The bag, which was connected to a copper tank filled with compressed oxygen, contained a material which would absorb the carbon dioxide produced in breathing, so that the same oxygen could be breathed repeatedly, replenished as necessary from the oxygen cylinder. By this means, a three-hour breathing supply could be provided.

Walker had heard of Fleuss' apparatus and invited him to Portskewett to make an attempt on the door in the headwall. Although Fleuss had little experience as a diver and had never worked under water, he had carried out experiments with his apparatus off the coast of the Isle of Wight in about 18 ft of water while tethered to a rowing boat on the surface.

Walker showed Fleuss drawings of the shafts and headings; Lambert would assist in the attempt. There was a rough platform about 150 ft from the top of the shaft, about 10 ft above the water in the bottom. A ladder ran down the shaft through a manhole in the platform. As Lambert was familiar with the layout of the workings, Fleuss asked him to descend to the mouth of the heading to act as guide. Lambert was wearing his normal diving equipment with helmet and air line. Fleuss' modified apparatus had a similar helmet, but inside it he wore a mask fitting tightly over his nose and mouth and connected by two hoses to the bag on his back. Supply air was taken in by the nose, the air exhaled by the mouth being returned to the backpack. Fleuss descended the ladder, but could not feel the bottom of the shaft. He let go and sank 5 or 6 ft into the darkness, then moved sideways to reach the wall of the shaft. He found himself standing on planks which covered a sump for the pumps. Some of the planks were broken and kept giving way beneath him.

Eventually he located Lambert and started his journey up the heading. There was a ditch on each side of the heading for drainage purposes, so it was impossible for him to feel his way along the walls. The only way would be on hands and knees, guided by the rails used for the skips; standing up in the darkness it was impossible to ascertain direction. Initially he sank into deep mud, then he had to clamber over a big fall of debris, leaving little room between it and the roof of the heading. Progress was slow and Fleuss' nerve was failing. He made two more attempts but then finally lost his nerve completely, asserting on his return that he would not make another attempt for £10,000.

*The Fleuss self-contained breathing apparatus, modified for use with a
diver's helmet and suit*
(Source: Siebe Gorman and Company Limited)

Walker was still determined to close the door and valves. He asked Fleuss to lend his apparatus to Lambert, overcoming Fleuss' initial opposition by reasoning that success would be the best possible advertisement for his invention. After some persuasion, Lambert agreed to make an attempt wearing the Fleuss apparatus. He donned the equipment and, with the guidance of Fleuss, made a few practice dives. Little was known at the time about the effects of breathing large quantities of oxygen. Later years would reveal that excess oxygen, particularly at depth and during periods of physical exertion, could induce convulsions and blackouts.

It was with considerable anxiety that Walker, on the afternoon of 8 November 1880, watched Lambert start his perilous journey. Fleuss sat on the edge of the manhole at the bottom of the shaft, counting off the minutes. Walker grew more and more anxious as the time passed. He had warned Lambert of the dangers of damaging the flimsy apparatus on the timbers in the heading, or by stumbling over a skip or debris. Suddenly, after an hour and a half, Lambert surfaced; he had reached the door, closed one of the valves and lifted one of the rails, but the second had defeated him. He was full of confidence and seemed unaware of the pioneering nature of his efforts, using little-tried equipment under such difficult circumstances. He was ready to go back to complete the work, but Fleuss needed to return to London for more oxygen and carbon dioxide absorbent.

On 10 November Lambert once again started down the heading, clutching a bar to prise up the second rail. An hour and twenty minutes later he returned, triumphant, showing little evidence of his ordeal. He had removed the rail, shut the door and screwed round the rod of the sluice valve to close it.

Elated by the success, Walker started the pumps and

carefully watched the floats which indicated the depth of water in the shafts. But after Lambert's triumph came disappointment; the water, even with all pumps running, was only falling at the rate of 3 in per hour. At high tide the pumps could only maintain a stable water level. The pressure on the pumps began to tell, and one of the pumps in the Old Shaft eventually broke down. Two attempts by Lambert to effect repairs to the pump underwater enabled it to run for a short time, but eventually Walker was forced to acknowledge that nothing could be done until the offending part of the pump was above the surface.

The water level dropped slowly, until it was possible to work on the pump. But conditions were far from ideal; as the men struggled to carry out repairs to the pump, a torrent of freezing water poured onto them from behind the shield in the upper heading.

With the pump working again the water level dropped quickly, and by 12 November the Iron Shaft was nearly empty. Walker was optimistic, but his good fortune was not to last; over the next month a succession of pump failures dogged further progress. It was not until 6 December that the water in the Iron Shaft was fully under control.

It was now possible for James Richards, the Cornish foreman of the pumps, to walk along the long heading under the river to the door that Lambert had closed. Soon the cause of Walker's frustrations became evident; water was pouring through the 12-in sluice valve in the wall. The valve must have been fully closed when Lambert reached it. He had given the valve the correct number of turns clockwise, but it had a left-hand thread and, instead of closing the valve, he had opened it fully. Closing the valve produced an immediate effect and the pumps could be slowed down, bringing the water fully under control for the first time since Walker had taken over the works in January 1880:

> No one but those who have been engaged in such a struggle can imagine the delight of all hands at the victory which it had taken us nearly twelve months to win.

It was now possible to explore the heading leading to the Great Spring. The doors in the shield were opened and, clad in diver's suits and wearing sou'westers instead of helmets, Joseph Talbot (the foreman of the miners), J. Clarke Hawkshaw (son of Sir John) and Walker clambered through the tiny opening into the heading as water cascaded through. Their lights revealed a fast flowing steam of water about a foot deep and the full width of the heading pouring towards them from the darkness ahead. The three men waded along the heading for about 200 yd. Soon they could see the smashed timbers and a huge quantity of debris about 3 or 4 ft deep where the Great Spring had broken in. The air in the heading was foul; breathing was difficult and the lights began to falter. Retracing their steps they selected an area of sound rock about 450 ft from the entrance to the heading. An 8 ft thick brick wall was to be built across the heading at this point, fitted with a heavy door and frame. Clay dams and timber troughs were necessary to divert the water during the construction of the wall, and materials had to be hauled along the water-filled heading on a raft. A pipe filled with compressed air was also needed to make working conditions more tolerable. On 4 January 1881 the heavy oak door in the wall was closed and the Great Spring imprisoned.

4 | *Changing Fortunes*

Considerable progress had been made in the provision of accommodation for the men. An additional number of small houses for married couples and children or lodgers, and semi-detached houses for foremen had been erected close to the works. A large house for the principal foreman, Joseph Talbot, and his family had been built on the banks of the river. Joe, like his father and five brothers, had spent most of his life building tunnels. He was critical of the idea of building tunnels through rock, voicing the opinion that they should only be made in soft ground.

Walker was a religious man who would regularly pray for guidance and the protection of the men on the works. He was a stern individual, but a man with great willpower and strength of character. He was deeply concerned for the spiritual wellbeing of his workforce, and to this end he built a mission hall to hold 250 people. Arrangements were made for a supply of preachers, with services on Wednesdays and Sundays, but Walker himself took every opportunity to lead prayer meetings in the hall. A day school and Sunday school had also been opened, with an attendance of forty by the end

Village scene
(Source: John Harvey)

of the year. The nearest public road, close to the Black Rock Hotel, was linked to the works and tradesmen from Caldicot and Chepstow called at the houses every day with provisions of all kinds, giving the new community the appearance of a well-established town.

The year 1881 opened on an optimistic note for work on the tunnel project. The headwalls had excluded all the water from the river heading and the heading inland containing the Great Spring. Despite this, pumping was still needed and required a continuous supply of coal by rail from the South Wales coalfields to feed the steam boilers, a dependence which caused problems early in the year.

On the afternoon of 18 January, Walker was returning to the works by express train from London when a massive snowstorm blew up, rapidly engulfing southern England. Progress beyond Swindon was impossible. The train was able to get through to Portskewett the following day, but by this time all the roads had been blocked and the branch line serving the works lay under 4 ft of snow. To make matters worse, a severe frost had set in. The small stock of coal held at the works rapidly dwindled and local supplies were soon exhausted. Building operations were at a standstill for nearly a fortnight, the meagre coal supplies being supplemented by timber from the works in an effort to keep the boilers and pumps running.

With the improvement in the weather, work got under-way once more. As a result of Sir John Hawkshaw's decision to lower the tunnel, the heading under the river was useless for drainage purposes as originally intended. It was also in a bad state of repair. Hawkshaw instructed Walker to enlarge the heading and to line it with brickwork to the point where it connected with the main tunnel, thus affording an additional facility for ventilating the tunnel on completion, whilst allowing the safe passage of men and materials during the course of the works.

A new shaft, to be called the 'New Winding Shaft', was commenced on the Welsh side, close to the existing excavations, and it was designed to connect with the enlarged river heading enabling far greater quantities of materials and debris to be handled. The enlargement of the heading to the headwall had been completed by April 1881. After releasing the water behind the headwall, Walker and Talbot swung open the door that Lambert had closed some five months earlier and clambered into the river heading. It was in reasonable condition, but as they made their way under the river the two men were confronted by an earlier roof fall, about 1¾ miles from the shaft, which blocked the heading and prevented further exploration. The air pipes along the side of the heading had been choked with dirt, making breathing laboured and the lights were only kept going with difficulty. Eventually the lights failed altogether, plunging the men into darkness and bringing into stark perspective the heroic exploits of Lambert in the previous year. Talbot, with Walker's hand on his shoulder, slowly groped his way back through the darkness to the shaft.

Before work could continue, the air pipe had to be cleared of debris and holes punched in it at intervals to allow air to reach all parts of the heading. But it would take nearly an hour for the men to push trolleys, loaded with materials or debris, the full length of the heading. Accordingly Walker ordered the men to take food with them so that they could remain underground for the whole of the ten-hour shift.

The Great Western Railway men, used to eight-hour shifts, were already unhappy about working an extra two hours per shift. The prospect of spending the whole shift in the stifling air of the tunnel, instead of coming up to the surface for their meals, precipitated a confrontation with Walker. Their discontent began to manifest itself when Walker's men were jeered as they prepared to go below. There then followed a series of assaults in the darkness of the headings. Walker was convinced that there had been ill-feeling ever since he had taken charge of the works. He sensed that some of the men wished he might fail in his efforts to rid the works of water, even to the extent of attributing some of the difficulties that he had encountered to the men that he had inherited at the start of the contract.

Finally, on Saturday 21 May 1881, the men congregated at the top of the main shaft and refused to go below. After a period of animated debate, they retired to a nearby public house. Suitably primed, the men made their way to the pay office and demanded a return to eight-hour shifts. Walker had a quick temper; he happened to be in the office at the time and he provides an insight into Victorian industrial relations. He refused to concede to the men's demands, ordering them to collect their pay and leave the works by the first available train. The works came to a standstill:

> One of the most alarming, if not the most serious
> catastrophe that has occurred in this district for many years
> . . . happened at an early hour on Monday morning, when
> the wooden pier at the Portskewett side of the New Passage
> Ferry caught fire and was quite consumed before the flames
> were got under control. A nightwatchman named John
> Henry Williams, aged 19 years, was employed to look after
> the pier and the approaches and on Sunday night he was on
> duty as usual. The porter's room at the pier head was
> occupied by him at intervals and on this occasion he left the

Severn Tunnel workers at the Black Rock Inn
(Source: Chepstow Museum)

room at half past twelve o'clock, visited the engine house, noticed that all was right and walked up the platform, finding nothing of an unusual character in any part of the premises. He then returned to the porter's room, which is opposite to the engine house and between 1.30 a.m. and 2.00 a.m. his attention was attracted by a sudden glare through a crack in the door. He threw open the door and no sooner had he done so than he perceived the pier in flames, which spread with great rapidity, fanned as they were by a breeze blowing from the east. Perceiving at a glance that the only way of saving his life was to rush through the burning material, he dashed along the platform, but as he proceeded his clothes caught fire, and . . . was so seriously injured that it was seen that he could not recover . . . he said that he was firmly convinced that the pier was set on fire wilfully as he had walked over the spot from whence the flames has issued only a short time before and everything then was as it should be. No train had passed over the pier since 4 o'clock on Sunday evening and no one but himself had any business on the pier afterwards . . . the origin of the fire remains a mystery. . . .

(*Chepstow Weekly Advertiser*, Saturday 28 May 1881)

Many attributed the fire to the striking workforce, but Walker remained sceptical, being of the opinion that the combination of dry weather and the careless discarding of a match, or sparks from one of the boilers used to power the luggage lift, had been the cause of the blaze. But the boilers were out, and the last train had been on the pier some hours before the outbreak of the fire. Later, in the same newspaper article, it was reported that miners and navvies from the Severn Tunnel works helped the fire brigade to fight the blaze.

The tunnel works remained silent. On the Tuesday fol-

Portskewett Pier with the works in the background
(Source: Walker, The Severn Tunnel)

lowing the pier fire, Walker brought pressure to bear on the strikers by ordering the carpenters, blacksmiths and other surface workers to stop work. One might reasonably suppose that the subsequent confrontation between the Great Western men and Walker's workmen was the incentive for the strikers to begin slowly drifting back: work quietly resumed without further trouble. Walker was convinced that his stand had been justified and that the disruptive members of the workforce had finally been disposed of.

Now only 130 yd separated England and Wales below the river. The headings were back in working condition after the roof fall, and Walker was in a position to start the construction of sections of the tunnel proper.

The finished tunnel, effectively a large tube lined with brickwork up to 3 ft thick, would be roughly circular in section and about 26 ft in diameter internally. The bottom of the tunnel, called the invert, a slightly flatter portion of lining, would carry the two railway tracks bedded on a layer of ballast – broken stone and gravel up to 4 ft thick. This would provide a flat surface over the curved invert, and a resilient bearing for the rails and sleepers.

The normal tunnelling procedure would be to drive a heading 7–9 ft square in a position close to the bottom of the proposed tunnel and then to open out to the full size of the tunnel by removing material upwards and sideways. All this work would have to be carried out while supporting the ground to a greater or lesser degree, depending upon circumstances, with substantial and often elaborate temporary timber support.

After Hawkshaw's decision to lower the tunnel by 15 ft, the original heading would be in the wrong place, near the top of the tunnel, making it necessary to remove material not only upwards and sideways, but downwards as well. Supporting the ground would be much more difficult. The problem was overcome by opening out upwards and sideways in the normal way to form the top half of the tunnel, which was then lined with brickwork to the required thickness. The top half of the tunnel secure, the bottom half could then be built by excavating downwards to the required level. The brick lining to the lower half of the tunnel was carried round the invert and up the sides to meet the upper lining, which in the meantime had been supported by the ground. Obviously the work would have to be done in short sections, otherwise there would be no support for the upper lining during the time that the lower lining was being built up to it. This process is known as underpinning.

The setting out of the lines and levels for the tunnel work was carried out by a mechanical and civil engineer called A.O. Schenk, the chief of Walker's engineering staff. It was a massive responsibility. In normal railway construction a tunnel would represent a very small part of the contract, just one item in several miles of railway, and as such the rate of work attained in its construction would be similar to the rest of the works. In larger tunnels, shafts would be sunk about a quarter of a mile apart, with headings driven from the bottom of the shafts in each direction until they were all joined. Any inaccuracies in line or level could be corrected when the headings were enlarged to the full-sized tunnel; the close spacing of the shafts would facilitate this, minimizing the chances of error. In the case of the Severn Tunnel, the circumstances were altogether different. If the work was to be completed on time it would be necessary to build finished tunnel sections at various points wherever and whenever possible. With the shafts on each side of the estuary nearly

CROSS SECTION OF TUNNEL

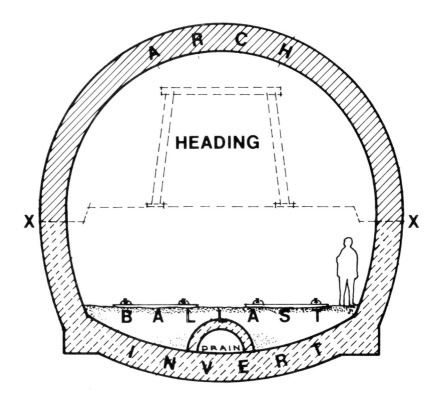

As a consequence of Hawkshaw's decision to lower the tunnel another 15 ft, the heading would be too high and the top of the tunnel above the line XX would have to be built first, with the invert and the sidewalls being built up to the underside of the arch afterwards
(Source: author)

2½ miles apart, the magnitude of the task facing Schenk can be appreciated.

In addition, although the tunnel would run under the estuary in a straight line, in order to join up with the existing railway on the Welsh side it would not only need to be built in a curve about 1½ miles in radius immediately it reached the shore, it would also need a gradient of 1 in 90 to take it under the river.

Straight sections of tunnel would be set out by lining up two plumb-lines reaching to the bottom of a shaft with a third further down the heading. It is interesting to note that, with wires 14 ft apart, an error of just 1/16 in on one side of the estuary would be magnified to a distance of nearly 5 ft at the shaft on the other side. For the curved portion of the tunnel, the centre line would be set out at ground level as a series of straight lines. The lines were then transferred below ground by the plumb-lines referred to earlier, the angles and lengths of the lines on the surface being reproduced along the heading. A special code of signals using railway lamps had to be evolved so that the observer could communicate with his assistant in the darkness of the heading.

One extraordinary piece of setting out by Schenk is recorded by Walker. The decision to lower the tunnel meant that the Iron Shaft had to be made deeper in order to pump water from the lower level. But all the time the shaft was fully operative, with pumps extracting water from the rest of the works. The only answer was to build a heading to a point below the bottom of the Iron Shaft, to construct the new section of the shaft, 18 ft in diameter, exactly below the existing one, and then to break upwards into it. After a careful survey, Schenk set out a point in the heading which represented the centre of the unseen Iron Shaft above and the

AT WORK IN THE TUNNEL

At work in the tunnel
(Source: author)

new section of shaft was built. In Walker's words: 'When a hole was broken through the roof into the Iron Pit, the point given did not vary one inch from the true centreline of the shaft.'

The full-sized tunnel was started in sections, or 'lengths' as they were termed, on the Sea Wall side of the river during the first part of 1881. The work proceeded without incident until the end of April. Then, as a gang of bricklayers were building the brick lining to a section of tunnel, the roof suddenly gave way and water burst into the workings. The river had broken in. Frantic attempts to plug the aperture from below were in vain; it would have to be located from above and stopped off while pumps dealt with the influx of water. The approximate location of the break-in could be ascertained; it had occurred in the bed of the Salmon Pool, a shallow area of water only about 3 ft deep at low tide.

A perfunctory examination of the murky waters of the pool failed to reveal the location of the hole, so Walker ordered about thirty of his men to hold hands and to walk waist deep across the pool, whereupon one of the men abruptly disappeared below the surface as he stepped into the void leading to the tunnel below. His subaqueous journey was arrested only by the grip of his colleagues on either side.

Walker had been wise not to be too hasty in linking the two headings below the river. He directed the pumps to be stopped at Sea Wall, thus allowing the river water to fill the eastern heading. This expedient would prevent water pouring continuously into the tunnel and enlarging the hole further. Clay, in layers and in bags, was then dumped over the hole at low tide, and the pumps restarted. The exercise was entirely successful; as the water level fell in the tunnel, the clay effectively stopped river water entering the workings.

Meanwhile the method of removing spoil from the works needed improving. The Great Western Railway originally employed men, called 'runners out', to push skips along the headings – a very expensive and time-consuming procedure with the long distances now involved. In the bottom heading to the west of the Shoots the gradient was quite shallow. Walker replaced the original light rails with heavier ones and introduced strong ponies to pull the skips, thus cutting haulage costs by 90 per cent. The ponies rapidly adapted to underground working and eventually needed very little guidance. But this arrangement would be unworkable in the eastern heading between the Shoots and Sea Wall on account of the steep 1 in 100 gradient of this section of tunnel. A mechanical means of spoil handling had to be devised. A steam-driven hauling engine was set up at the top of the Sea Wall shaft, driving, via pulleys, an endless wire rope which was taken down the shaft, carried more than a mile along the heading and back again to the engine. The rope was kept constantly in motion, it being necessary only to hook a full skip onto the ascending rope at the bottom end of the heading. The skip, on arrival at the shaft, was disengaged and pushed clear; an empty one, or one loaded with materials, was then hooked onto the descending rope. As many as 200 skips, some full, some empty, might be in motion at any given time. The system worked perfectly and proved to cost half as much as pony haulage.

An air supply for both the rock drills and the workmen had to be pumped through iron pipes up to 1¾ miles long to the working face in the heading. The hot, damp conditions were exacerbated by the fumes from the explosives used in blasting a way through the rock. Dynamite produces con-siderable amounts of noxious fumes. The *Chepstow Weekly*

Pit pony and men
(Source: John Harvey)

Advertiser records an incident which occurred during an earlier stage of the tunnel works:

> On Wednesday afternoon two miners, James Maggs (aged 50) and Oliver Sheppard (aged 45), who had been at work in the Middle Shaft of the Severn Tunnel Works, succumbed to the injurious effects of inhaling the fumes caused by the use of dynamite in the workings. The poor fellows were so overcome that they had to be brought to the bank (i.e. the top of the shaft), where they died in a comparatively short space of time. . . .

(Saturday 27 September 1879)

Walker elected to use 'tonite', a carefully prepared explosive, instead of dynamite. It was not affected by cold or moisture, was conveniently packaged and produced minimal amounts of noxious fumes. A great deal of skill was needed to ensure that the correct quantity of explosive was used. A hole would be drilled into the rock to a suitable depth and an appropriate number of packages of tonite placed in it, this being detonated by fuse. Too little explosive and the process would have to be repeated, too much and there was a danger of loosening rock outside the area being worked.

An alternative to tonite was tested during the course of the works. Lime cartridges had been used with considerable success in coal mining operations; compressed lime was placed in a large borehole and water pumped in. The ensuing chemical reaction caused the lime to swell and gas to be generated, splitting material away from the working face. During one such test in the Severn Tunnel, Joe Talbot was watching the hole being packed and water being pumped in, when without warning the charge of lime blew out. It hit

Talbot full in the face, filling his eyes with the caustic compound. For two days it was feared that his sight would be lost. Fortunately he made a full recovery, but the incident served to convince Walker that the lime cartridge method must be rejected.

The effectiveness of the ventilation to the works below ground was put under scrutiny in 1881 when a Severn Tunnel worker, John Hopkins, died from inflammation of the lungs, allegedly caused by the poor working conditions. An inquest was held which brought into question not only the working conditions but also the ten-hour shift, the cause of the strike at the works:

> I complain of the finding of the jury, that the inflammation of the lungs of the deceased, John Hopkins, was occasioned by his inhaling foul air. Hopkins had been here about six weeks. He had never been working in the long heading away from the shaft and in the place where he worked there was always a natural current of air almost equal to the air above ground . . . 3 steam engines are constantly employed pumping fresh air to the workmen. The air in the workings is better than I have ever known in tunnel work and in this I speak from an experience in tunnels of 34 years, and I must say that I think it is an anomaly that a village jury of persons totally inexperienced in such matters, who decline to visit the works, and who do not hear the evidence of responsible persons in charge of them, should have summarily pronounced judgement on such a matter. I should be very pleased, Sir, if you, or any friends of yours, would visit the works and judge whether it is possible that any men employed in them could suffer from foul air. I maintain that it is impossible. . . .

> (Letter from Walker, dated 9 August 1881, to the editor of the *Chepstow Weekly Advertiser*)

I see that Mr T.A. Walker complains in your column . . . if you, Mr Editor, lived in our village, you would see daily poor fellows, hardly able to walk to the doctor, passing by. I know personally of one man that was working down in the same place as the deceased and he was obliged to give up the work owing to the foul air. He has worked underground for 8 years and he tells me he never, when miles underground, was in a place where the air was so impure. Add to all this the knowledge that since the tunnelling has begun, three deaths have resulted from inflammation of the lungs caused by foul air, I think, Mr Editor, when two more men were lying dead from inflammation of the lungs after two or three days illness, (I am told hale hearty men), we were only doing our duty in calling for an inquest . . . our reason for referring to the dispute between Mr Walker and his men was to show that many of them had said the hours were much too long to work in such impure air. In the evidence given the air compressors worked the boring machine first before the men got the benefit of them and they complained the air reached them quite hot and smelling of the oil . . . perhaps the lives of a few such men as the deceased are not worth our troubling about, but there is a feeling in common that the village jury have, and that is that these men were the breadwinners of large families and if somebody is snatched from them they must therefore become a burden on someone. Which, I might say, the contractor or the taxpayers?

(Letter dated 16 August 1881 from F.G. Sealey, builder, of Caldicot, to the editor of the *Chepstow Weekly Advertiser*)

Sir Daniel Gooch was a regular visitor: 'Friday September 23 1881 – I spent today at the Severn Tunnel. The works are progressing favourably. I went into a finished part of the tunnel, it looks well. We have had a fine day. . . .' Three days after this diary entry, at 10.00 p.m. on 26 September 1881, the western heading was driven through to join the eastern heading, linking England and Wales below the Severn for the first time. This achievement also gave the opportunity to improve the ventilation of the tunnel. Walker purchased a huge fan, 18 ft in diameter and 7 ft wide, and fixed it at the top of one of the shafts on the west bank. With the heading now completed under the river, fresh air could be drawn through over 2 miles of workings, improving the conditions below ground immeasurably.

The new shaft, 18 ft in diameter, on the western side of the river, had been fitted with two large iron lift cages, each capable of transporting four laden skips or forty men between ground level and the workings below. Work also continued in both directions from the Five Miles Four Chains shaft; to the east the heading stretched to within 26 ft of the Great Spring. It was strenuous work; the rock was hard, with frequent pockets of water, and considerable pumping power was needed to keep the headings dry.

Brick production had been further refined; within half an hour of the material being excavated from the workface below, it had been made into bricks on the surface, ready for drying. The new village continued to expand. By the end of 1881, more than forty houses and cottages had been built. The existing communal facilities were augmented by a coffee house and reading room. A large office had been erected, together with other facilities to assist the works: a sawmill and carpenters' shop, stables for twenty horses with fitting and blacksmith's shop, and cabins at the top of each shaft for meals and changing. The drying of waterproof clothing or flannels, supplied by Walker, and the guarding of the men's

Men and boys at the brickworks
(Source: John Harvey)

own clothes, was superintended by a man in each cabin. Six temporary timber houses were constructed near the brickyard for the men employed there, and additional roads had been built. The village, though by now well established, in fact had no official name until a post and telegraph office was opened in 1882. Henceforth the village was known as Sudbrook. On the other side of the river, land could not be leased or purchased adjacent to the workings, so wooden houses were built on the line of the tunnel; brick houses would have been prone to damage through subsidence as the tunnelling work proceeded below them.

In January 1882, Sir John Hawkshaw was able to report to the Great Western directors that about 500 ft of the full-sized tunnel had been finished. In addition to this, the top half of the tunnel had been completed for a distance of over 1,500 ft. But this represented only a tiny proportion of the final total of nearly 23,000 ft. It was necessary for more men to be taken on to increase the rate of progress; over two years had passed since Walker took charge of the contract and this time had predominantly been spent clearing the works of water, repairing the headings and improving working conditions. On 5 January, Walker wrote to Hawkshaw:

> I would not return to the subject again if I were not compelled to do so . . . I am quite sure it is not your desire that the progress of the works should be crippled by my being constantly short of money and I have told you the simple truth that I have paid out of pocket more than £50,000 beyond what I have received from the Company.

Great care had to be exercised by foremen and miners while building full-sized sections of the tunnel. Towards the end of January 1882, one of the sections of tunnel under the river had been excavated and carefully supported by large timbers in preparation for the bricklayers to start the brick lining. Without warning a huge mass of material suddenly slid out, knocking the timber supports away, and a section of the tunnel collapsed. It was a desperate situation; the collapse had occurred deep under the river. But the bed of the river remained secure and the roof was rapidly made safe with timber. However, despite the fact that it took only a fortnight to open out the section of tunnel, two months would pass before the debris was cleared and all the supporting timber re-established. The tunnel was built in more than 1,500 separate sections along its 7,664 yd length; it is remarkable, and a credit to all concerned, that only this one length collapsed during the entire course of the contract.

On 29 April 1882, the *Chepstow Weekly Advertiser* reported progress:

> The progress which the works in connection with the tunnel under the Severn are making may be indicated by the large number of men employed, as, since the Easter holidays, Mr Walker, the contractor, has put on many additional hands, so that there are nearly 2,000 workmen engaged in different parts of the undertaking. It is a difficult matter to accommodate such a large number of persons in the surrounding villages, as several men have families. Extra house room is accordingly being provided near the works, and already about a hundred houses are built. A great improvement in the lighting arrangements has taken place, the incandescent electric lights – a Swan's patent – having to a great extent superceded the old lamps in the workshops above ground and in the tunnelling. . . . There is water still in the shaft, but the contractor does not make much account of the quantity perceptible, as the pumping machinery is of

excellent character, and much more formidable obstacles than those that now present themselves have been overcome in the last year or two by perseverance.

But on the same date it was reported that:

A virulent fever has broken out among the workmen at the Severn Tunnel. Two have died.

Earlier in the year one of the large cottages had been converted into a hospital, under the charge of a resident doctor and nurse. In the summer of 1882 a purpose-built hospital was commenced. It would incorporate a residence for a matron and rooms for the resident doctor, a nursing sister and an assistant nurse, together with wards for general and emergency use and an operating room. The new hospital would prove to be invaluable for the treatment of accidents and diseases in the works. Walker was a regular visitor to the hospital to give support and encouragement to the patients.

There were constant reminders of the dangers inherent in tunnel works in the local press:

Early on Wednesday morning, George Owen, a middle-aged man . . . was conveyed to Bristol Royal Infirmary suffering from serious injuries to his arm and face, caused through an explosion of dynamite at the Severn Tunnel works. It was found necessary to amputate the sufferer's left arm and we have heard that he has since died.

(*Chepstow Weekly Advertiser*, 10 June 1882)

In July of 1882, Hawkshaw was able to report that 800 yards of tunnel, and the top half of the tunnel for another 500

Building the cuttings
(Source: John Harvey)

Navvies with steam excavator
(Source: John Harvey)

yards, had been completed, and a start had been made on the massive cutting leading to the tunnel mouth on the Gloucestershire side of the river. As a consequence of his decision to lower the level of the tunnel, more than twice the amount of material would have to be excavated, a total of over 800,000 cu yd – in excess of a million tons. A quarter of this would be used to build Richardson's sea defences around the top of the cutting. An army of navvies would be required to do the work.

The term 'navvy' originates from the eighteenth-century navigators, the men who carved a network of canals across the country before the coming of the railways. Some experienced railway navvies followed the line, but mainly they were rural labourers recruited from the locality. It was a tough way of life. Navvies had the reputation for boisterous and unruly behaviour in previously quiet towns and villages, and for terrorizing the local inhabitants, a reputation which recent research shows is somewhat exaggerated. There is little doubt that navvies were heavy drinkers, but this has to be put into the context of an age where drunkenness, crime and violence were common.

As the century wore on and contractors became more caring, the navvies' behaviour mellowed, but some traditions remained. A navvy would dress in moleskin trousers, double canvas shirt, waistcoat (often bright in colour), jacket, hobnail boots, cap, have a gaudy handkerchief tied around his neck, and would invariably be known by an alias or nickname which was usually derived from place of origin (Yorkey, Lanks, Bristol Jack, Devon Bill), background or appearance (Ginger Bill, Pigtail Punch, Bones). Their work rate was phenomenal; in one day a navvy would load 20 tons of material into wagons.

Reports of crime and drunkenness appeared regularly in the *Chepstow Weekly Advertiser*. On 30 September 1882, Severn Tunnel workers ran amok in a nearby beerhouse. For many crimes, punishment could be harsh:

> William Griffiths, 18, described as a labourer working at the Severn Tunnel works, was charged with stealing the sum of £32 19s. 5½d . . . he pleaded guilty, and was sentenced to 18 months hard labour, a previous conviction being recorded against him.

> (21 October 1882)

One bizarre consequence of the tunnel works was the draining of the wells in the vicinity, thus depriving the inhabitants of their source of fresh water. This might have posed an interesting legal problem. In October 1882, Walker wrote to the local surveyor:

> I think it right to take this opportunity of stating that as an act of grace and favour, in consideration of the inconvenience caused to the inhabitants of Portskewett and Caldecot by the drainage of their wells, a water main has been laid to each village to furnish a supply. . . .

The timber houses on the centreline of the tunnel on the Gloucestershire side of the river were built on a thick layer of gravel, a material which is difficult to tunnel through as it flows easily, particularly when saturated with water. Fortunately the gravel did not extend to the heading below, which was being built through solid rock. But the margin of safety provided by the roof of the heading was far less than had been anticipated; only 6 in of rock instead of the 6 ft assumed. In the middle of November 1882, the men working on the heading had been withdrawn to work elsewhere. Shortly after the occupants of the houses, workmen, their wives and lodgers, had settled down for the night, the thin rock layer forming the roof of the heading suddenly gave way and a fluid mixture of gravel and water deluged into the heading. On the surface, a brick chimney between two houses shot down vertically into the ground, leaving the buildings hanging precariously over the hole. It must have been an alarming experience for the sleeping residents. Many thought that there was an earthquake, threw open windows and jumped out. Walker was wise to build timber houses; the integrity and inherent flexibility of this form of construction prevented a major catastrophe and there were no injuries other than a sprained ankle for one of the jumpers. Subsequently Walker was much amused to receive a vast inventory of watches and money, which had apparently disappeared into the bowels of the earth in the pockets of trousers and waistcoats hung on nails on the chimney breast.

Walker's attention to the spiritual wellbeing of his employees was meeting with great success. Walker himself ran Bible classes for the men. The mission room, although enlarged, was regularly packed with 500 people every Sunday evening. On 26 November 1882 the room was crowded as usual, the congregation sweltering in the heat created by the hot air flues passing under the aisles:

> At about three o'clock on Monday morning it was discovered that a chapel at the Severn Tunnel Works . . . capable of holding 400 to 500 persons, was on fire. The flames, after the discovery, made rapid progress, and although a large number of workpeople employed at the

Children outside the old mission hall
(Source: John Harvey)

works used all endeavours to subdue the fire, their efforts were unavailing and the edifice was totally destroyed, including an organ which had been but recently purchased by Mr Walker. The loss, which is estimated to be a considerable amount, is, we have been given to understand, covered by insurance. The origin of the fire is supposed to have been the overheating of the flues underneath the flooring, connected with the heating apparatus. . . .

(*Chepstow Weekly Advertiser*, 2 December 1882)

Typhoid outbreaks continued to cause concern. The same newspaper reported that:

. . . two cases of typhoid fever had been admitted into the (Bristol) Royal Infirmary during the week and the disease in one case was clearly contracted from the Severn Tunnel works. Another death from fever of a child had occurred in the city, but the medical man was not certain whether the disease was contracted from the father, who worked in the Severn Tunnel. The contractor for the works, Mr T.A. Walker . . . stated that no doubt the source of the fever cases at the Severn Tunnel was to be traced to the fact that all the sewage of 20 or 30 houses within a mile of the works emptied itself into the open rheen (stream), which was the only drinking water of many of the inhabitants.

The morning after the mission hall fire, Walker sketched plans for a much larger replacement, gave orders for materials and by ten o'clock, on land that had been leased for additional houses, his men began the construction of a new hall. Within three hours of starting work, the foundations were finished. By one o'clock the masons were able to start building the walls; work continued night and day, in cold frosty weather, under the light of electric lamps. Forty-eight

The new mission hall, built in just three weeks in 1882
(Source: John Harvey)

large windows and eight doors were made and fixed, and benches to seat a thousand people were provided. On 17 December, less than three weeks after fire had consumed the old mission hall, the first service was held in the new building.

During the course of construction of the new hall, Walker was faced with another crisis. Just before 1.00 p.m. on 2 December, six days after the fire, he was leaving the hospital after visiting some of his men when he was met by one of his office staff in a state of panic, exclaiming that the tunnel had collapsed. Walker rushed to the shaft to find between three and four hundred men milling around in a state of shock. Some were exhausted and bruised, gasping for breath, hardly able to speak. Others watched as the big lift cage arrived with more men from below. Some had lost part of their clothing. Walker turned anxiously towards one of the foremen who had just arrived from below. Where had the river come in? What had he seen? The foreman had been working in the long heading beyond the Shoots. Surely if he had been working there he would have seen a break-in at the Shoots? Beyond the Shoots the river was shallow, dry at high tide. A break-in here could be cured with clay in a similar manner to the Salmon Pool. The foreman of the pumps was puzzled; there had been no increase in the water being handled by the pumps, and the water being discharged into the river was the same colour and in the same quantity as before. Walker decided to go below, accompanied by two of his staff.

As the cage jolted to a halt after the 200-ft journey to the bottom of the shaft, the three men were witness to an amazing sight. The heading was perfectly dry, and sitting on a piece of timber at one side were four or five men quietly cleaning their boots. In the meantime Joe Talbot had descended an iron staircase in one of the other shafts and made his way up the long river heading. Strewn around the floor of the heading were hats, leggings, waistcoats and scarves while ponies stood calmly by the abandoned skips. What on earth had happened?

The fear of a river break-in was always uppermost in the minds of the miners, working a mile or more from the shaft in a confined space, water dripping from rocks above their heads and running water at their feet, with only a flickering light to work by, and the reassuring muffled thump of the distant pumps, all the time maintaining a constant vigil for an unusual sound. Then from the darkness of the heading imagine the echo of timbers being thrown down, cries of warning and the sound of men running back to the shaft. Small groups would become bigger groups, probably three or four hundred men in total, shouting with fear and desperation, and, as the wide sections of completed tunnel give way to narrow linking headings, battling to get through the openings, standing on anyone unfortunate enough to stumble or be thrown to the ground. The ponies, alarmed by the screams of the men, galloping blindly along the headings, trampling on the prostrate bodies of men fighting to regain their feet, and clothes being torn off and cast aside to prevent the wearer from being dragged down by the impending deluge of water. . . .

But where was the water? Gradually Walker was able to piece together a reliable account of what had happened. There was always a fair quantity of water present in the workings. On this occasion the free passage of water to the pumps had been restricted by debris at one point in the heading. The foreman on the Gloucestershire side had

The panic
(Source: *Engineering Wonders of the World*)

ordered the debris to be removed, causing the water which had been dammed back to pour rapidly down the heading. Seeing a wave of water coming towards him further down the heading, one of the men shouted a warning. . . .

The work rate continued to improve, and men were now active throughout the full length of the tunnel. In January 1883, Sir John Hawkshaw was able to report to the Great Western directors that over three-quarters of a mile of tunnel had been completed. The top half of the tunnel had also been finished for a distance of over half a mile in addition to this and some progress had been made with the cutting on the English side of the river.

Reminders of the hazards of tunnelling continued. In December 1882, two men lost their lives in separate incidents when they fell down shafts at the works. An even more serious incident occurred at the beginning of February 1883 in the Five Miles Four Chains shaft:

> John Nash, labourer, was indicted for killing and slaying Timothy Yates, Francis Hyall, Charles Smith, John Shape and Richard Hanks . . . at about 1.30 a.m. on 9th February the prisoner received several loaded skips from the men working below and was about to return one of these after its contents had been removed . . . the empty skip fell down the pit onto a cage full of men who were waiting at the bottom to be drawn up. The consequence was that the five men were killed and several injured. . . .
>
> (*Chepstow Weekly Advertiser*, 4 August 1883)

There were two cages in the shaft. One had arrived at the top loaded with skips filled with material destined for the brickworks, the second was at the bottom. After removing the full skips, Nash clearly forgot which position held the empty cage with the result that he pushed an empty skip over the edge of the shaft onto the cage below. It was testified that he was 'a good, steady fellow and had never been complained of'. He was found not guilty, but 'a great gloom has been cast over the works in the neighbourhood of Portskewett and Caldecot in consequence of the disaster.'

In a lighter vein, efforts were being made to combat drinking:

> Severn Tunnel Total Abstinance Society – Amidst the rapid strides which the temperance cause is making throughout the country it is gratifying to note that the above Society is continually adding to its numbers, and under its auspices the advantages of temperance are constantly brought before the employees at the Severn Tunnel Works.
>
> (*Chepstow Weekly Advertiser*, 24 February 1883)

5 | *The Final Assault*

Construction of the tunnel in the vicinity of the Great Spring now needed to be tackled. At the end of May 1883 an attempt was made to open the door in the headwall that had been built some eighteen months previously, but debris which had fallen behind it made it impossible to open. A small hole about a foot across was broken through the door, releasing water under pressure which brought with it large quantities of material. The flow was interrupted intermittently by larger pieces of rock, which had to be laboriously broken up before they would pass through the hole in the door. After about two months it became evident that little progress was being made. Another heading was therefore built below the original and a hole broken upwards to release the water and to give access to the area behind the headwall. An inspection revealed that the heading had collapsed for a distance of about 50 or 60 ft, leaving a cavern above the fallen material large enough to swallow a large house. Much repair work was needed before work on the tunnel in this area could proceed.

In July 1883 Hawkshaw was able to report considerable progress to the directors. Nearly 1½ miles of tunnel were finished and the top half of the tunnel was completed for another three-quarters of a mile. A quarter of a million cubic yards of material had been excavated to form part of the cutting on the English side of the river, while another 20,000 cu yd had been removed on the Welsh side. There was thus a great sense of optimism on the works. However, in early October all hopes of a rapid completion of the tunnel were dashed:

A most serious accident occurred at the Severn Tunnel works on Wednesday night. At six o'clock, just as the night shift was going to work, a very large fresh-water spring, or, as it is supposed, a subterranean reservoir, was tapped in the heading on the Portskewett side of the river going towards Newport. It was under the land, and near the place where a large spring was tapped some four years ago. Up to Wednesday they had been working at the old spring, which had been dammed back by means of a wall, and was kept well under by the tremendous pumping power which Mr Walker, the contractor, had at his command – pumps capable of raising 11,000 gallons a minute. The water burst in on Wednesday night about 80 yards from the old spring, and it is, therefore, the impression that the two springs are connected. The water poured in with a volume four times the size of the former inundation, and that came in, it is stated, as big as a man's body . . . the whole distance flooded is about a mile and a half. The water has extended to within half a mile of the workings on the Bristol side, but has been stopped from making further progress by a thick brick wall, which was quickly built up on Thursday . . . there are no men injured, but three ponies were drowned, five being rescued by the men, who pluckily waded up to their waists in water to get them out. There are four thousand men engaged at the works, 600 of whom are thrown out of work . . . it will not be known for three or four days whether the present pumping power will be sufficient to cope with it.

(*Chepstow Weekly Advertiser, Saturday*
13 October 1883)

The water had broken in at the bottom of the workface of the heading as the night gang were loading skips with rocks dislodged by blasting. A huge wave swept the men and the skips through the open door of a headwall and along the heading until it opened out into a full-sized section of finished tunnel. Only then could they struggle to their feet as the water rushed along the bottom of the tunnel in a bright clear river, 16 ft or more wide, until it reached the shaft where it poured over the edge to fall more than 40 ft to the bottom with a deafening roar. The headwall and door had been built for just such a contingency as this, but when the men tried to fight their way back to the door to close it by clinging to the timbers supporting the heading, the inrush of water swirled around them nearly chest deep with such force that all attempts to reach the headwall failed.

Walker was at home when one of the foremen called to give him the bad news. He immediately went to the works and descended the shaft. To his relief the water was fresh; it was not the river that had broken in. But for the time being, the pumps were being rapidly drowned. Calculations showed that water was coming in at two-and-a-half times the rate that the pumps could remove it.

In two days the water had completely drowned the works under the river. The headings and tunnel being built from the Five Miles Four Chains, Marsh and Hill shafts were fortunately not yet connected to one another or to the section

under the river and thus escaped the flooding, as did the
works on the Gloucestershire side of the river; this was
primarily on account of the upward gradient of the tunnel
and heading, although the big headwall referred to in the
newspaper report had been built across the tunnel just west of
the Sea Wall Shaft as a precaution. But even as the level of the
water was rising in the section under the river, the largest of
the pumps at Five Miles Four Chains broke down and that
section of the works also became flooded. That left only the
workings connected with the Sea Wall, Marsh and Hill shafts
operational.

On 13 October thirty-one-year-old Charles Hawkins
stepped into the cage at the bottom of the Sea Wall Shaft
ready to come to the surface:

> On Saturday evening a labourer employed at the Severn
> Tunnel Works at the New Passage was killed whilst being
> drawn up the Sea Wall shaft. The cage is capable of
> containing about ten men, but on this occasion the deceased
> was the only occupant, and it is supposed that during the
> ascent he thrust his head outside, and in the rapid passage
> through the lift it came into collision with the side of the
> shaft. When the cage arrived at the surface the man was
> dead.
>
> (*Western Daily Press*, Monday 15 October 1883)

Three days later, a few lines tucked away between the news
reports in the *Western Daily Press* gave the weather forecast:

> England, S.W. (and S. Wales): South westerly to westerly
> winds, strong to a gale. Squally, showery, changeable. . . .

about 450 yd of tunnel had been completed at the bottom

of the Marsh Shaft. At about 7 p.m. on 17 October a large number of men had made their descent ready to begin the night shift. On the surface the predicted fierce storm was blowing from the south-west. Close to the shaft were a number of small cottages, some of stone and timber, others of brick, mostly single-storey. Without warning, out of the darkness, across the lowlands between the shaft and the river, came a huge tidal wave. It swirled around and into the houses, engulfing furniture, and children had to be plucked from the beds in which they were sleeping and carried upstairs. One man took a litter of young pigs up to his bedroom to save them.

William Gould was responsible for operating the lift cages in the Marsh Shaft. Shortly after seven o'clock the night-watchman came to warn him of the impending high tide. Gould sent a man down the shaft in one of the cages to warn the others that the tide was surrounding the shaft. As a second cage carrying another man was despatched to the bottom, the first cage returned carrying three men. But by now the water had poured into the shed containing the lift engines, quenched the boilers, and was heading towards the top of the shaft. Morgan Harris, a bricklayer, was at work in the tunnel when he heard the torrent of water. He hastened with others to the bottom of the shaft to find the lift cage immobilised. Harris began to climb the ladder at the side of the 100 ft deep shaft, but a cascade of icy water forced him back. A chain was thrown down from above to help the men in their ascent and several managed to struggle to the top successfully. John Bartlett, a forty-eight-year-old labourer, better known as 'Fighting Barney', made an attempt to climb the ladder as the water continued to pour down. After a short time he returned and collapsed with exhaustion, oblivious to the words of his colleagues and showing no signs of life. Harris and two others then fought their way to the top of the shaft, clinging to the ladder with one hand and the chain with the other. The climb was an exhausting one and the men were in a state of shock as they were grabbed by willing hands at the surface. More men began the arduous ascent, until about thirty had escaped. But Bartlett was dead, the level of the water in the tunnel was rising and over seventy men were still below. Their only course of action was to retreat up the gradient to a timber platform built for constructing the upper part of the tunnel some distance from the shaft. The water continued to rise until it was only 8 ft from the roof of the tunnel. By now more help had arrived at the surface and the tide was at last receding. A dam was rapidly thrown up around the top of the shaft using clothing, timber, sacks and anything else that came to hand.

A young engineer named Formby climbed down the ladder in the shaft and a small boat was lowered down to him end on, since the shaft was not wide enough to take it level. The boat as a consequence filled with water when it reached the bottom and had to be baled out. He was helped by others with lights and the men eventually clambered aboard. Initially there was just enough room to paddle the boat below the roof of the tunnel, but with the upward slope of the tunnel conditions improved and they were able to make their way through the drowned workings to their imprisoned colleagues. But soon their progress was halted by large timbers across the tunnel, and it was necessary to return to the shaft to collect a saw to cut through the obstacles. An eyewitness later described the plight of the trapped men:

The scene below was a most pitiable one. Some of the men

shrieked at the danger, and others, while waiting to be rescued, sang hymns and prayed.

(*Western Daily Press*, Monday 22 October 1883.)

A saw was obtained and a start made on cutting through the offending timbers, but such were the pressures of their mission that a grip was lost on the saw and it dropped out of sight below the surface of the water. Another saw was found and in time the nightmare was over; by the morning of 18 October all the men had been ferried to the shaft and returned safely to the surface, together with the body of Fighting Barney. It was remarkable that more lives had not been lost.

The tidal wave had not only swamped the works at the Marsh Shaft, it had covered the lowlands on both sides of the river. Richardson's sea walls had not been completed around the top of the cutting at the western end of the tunnel and the excavations were completely flooded.

The unusually high tide was commented on from many sources:

So high a tide has not been known for a hundred years.

(Diary of Sir Daniel Gooch)

Last night Bristol was visited by an extraordinarily high tide which flooded roads, dwellings and warehouses and resulted in a somewhat serious amount of damage to property. The tides for several days have been high, but last evening's not only eclipsed them but exceeded the highest reached in living memory of many of those connected with dock matters.

(*Western Daily Press*, Thursday 18 October 1883)

The rescue
(Source: *Engineering Wonders of the World*)

And, at the inquest on Fighting Barney:

> Another of those present mentioned that it had been stated
> that no such tide had been known at Tintern since 1795.
> Probably not many recollected that . . .

> (*Western Daily Press*, 22 October 1883)

These observations bring to mind the research of Charles
Richardson many years before, and the cynicism which
greeted his proposal for sea walls around the top of the
cuttings.

On the morning of 18 October the works lay in a worse
condition than they had been since January 1881. The *Western
Daily Press* echoed the sentiments of all who were connected
with the works:

> The past fortnight has been a disastrous period at the Severn
> Tunnel works and the courage of the contractor (Mr
> Walker) and his representative (Mr Kenway) has been put to
> a severe test. . . . The old saying that 'misfortunes never
> come singly' has again been confirmed, and it is to be hoped
> . . . that the time will not be long ere the tunnel will be
> cleared of water and the contractor will be able to resume
> operations in the parts that have been flooded.

> (Saturday 20 October)

After carrying out repairs, pumping again began at the Five
Miles Four Chains and Marsh shafts; by 23 October work
was once more resumed at the bottom of both. But if the
pumps were to be effective against the Great Spring and the
works under the river cleared of water, the door in the

The flooded Monmouthshire cutting
(Source: John Harvey)

headwall to the west of Sudbrook would have to be closed.

Walker again called upon the services of Alexander Lambert. Water was allowed to rise in the shaft so that the flow through the door in the headwall would be sufficiently subdued to enable Lambert to walk along the heading against the force of the current. On 29 October 1883, he donned his Fleuss apparatus and descended into the blackness of the flooded workings. But he found it impossible to reach the door, possibly due to ill-health, occasioned in Walker's opinion by the stress of recent salvage work in Australia, from where Lambert had recently returned. The following day he made another attempt in normal divers' dress with an airline, assisted by two other divers. This time he was more successful; he managed to reach the door and started to close it, but the current of water which was still flowing through the door opening caught the door, causing it to swing shut with an almighty crash. Later, according to Richardson, 'When the door slammed the concussion was terrific and made him see all the stars of heaven in his helmet.'

The success was reported to the directors by Hawkshaw:

After several abortive attempts we got the bottom door shut against the influx of water . . . and the water has been rapidly lowered . . . unless something occurs which I don't foresee or expect, the men will soon be at work again under the Severn.

When the Great Spring first flooded the works, Walker was of the opinion that the pumping power he had provided would meet with any future contingency, but recent events had dramatically changed the situation. Richardson lay the blame for the increased influx of water squarely on the shoulders of Hawkshaw; it had been the latter's decision to lower the tunnel and that had caused a substantial increase in the pressure of water from the Great Spring.

It was clear that the already considerable pumping power at Walker's disposal would need to be more than doubled before the tunnel could be finished. He made enquiries throughout the mining districts of various parts of the country and eventually four big beam engines were obtained from Harvey's of Hayle in Cornwall. Three of these would be erected at Sudbrook over the Old Shaft, which would now be used exclusively for pumping, the New Shaft reverting to a winding shaft solely for the transport of men and materials. The fourth engine would be at Five Miles Four Chains. Four pumphouses would be needed; each would be a substantial brick and stone building as big as a four-storey house with walls 2 ft 6 in thick. The end walls to carry the massive engine beams would be 5 ft thick.

Ten big Lancashire boilers about 30 ft long and 7 ft in diameter were also purchased to produce the vast quantities of additional steam necessary for powering the new pumps. The provision of this new equipment cost more than £16,000 at a time when Walker was already £100,000 out of pocket.

Clearly the erection of the buildings and equipment would take some considerable time; little could be done below the river until the end of 1883. The Great Spring only affected part of the tunnel below the river; elsewhere progress continued at such a rapid pace that bricks could not be obtained at a fast enough rate to keep up with the bricklayers lining the tunnel, even though over 1,200,000 bricks were being delivered to the works every month. Some of these came from the Cattybrook Brickworks near Bristol (a brickworks started by Charles Richardson in 1864); some

View of the works. In the middle of the picture, with open door, is the contractor's office. Bottom left is the fitting shop, with the smithy behind it. Beyond the smithy is a row of early cottages. To the right, at the front of the picture, are the stores and stables block with the carpenter's shop behind. At mid-distance on the right is the new mission hall, with rows of terraced houses stretching into the distance
(Source: Walker, The Severn Tunnel)

came from Staffordshire, an area well known for producing high strength bricks; the rest were made at the works. Negotiations led to further supplies being obtained from Staffordshire, increasing the total to well over two million bricks a month, a quantity which would have been sufficient for the construction of nearly two hundred terraced houses every four weeks. On the eastern end of the tunnel, the construction was supervised with great efficiency by John Price, the principal foreman, Joe Talbot's equivalent on the English side. Price was an intelligent, well-read man who had gained experience in tunnelling while working on the East London Railway under Walker's direction in the 1870s, during which time a fall had badly damaged his knee, leaving him slightly lame.

By the beginning of the New Year, 1884, Hawkshaw was able to report that just over 2 miles of tunnel (nearly half the finished length) had been completed. The upper half of another mile of tunnel was also finished. Three steam navvies (steam-driven mechanical excavators) were now at work, two on the Welsh side, one on the English side, and a total of 350,000 cubic yards (about half a million tons) of material had been removed from the two cuttings. Another steam navvy would soon be available, augmented by seven steam locomotives and a huge contingent of human navvies excavating material and loading it into wagons.

Life for these increasing numbers of workers and the other residents of Sudbrook was enhanced socially by various events:

These entertainments take place in the School Room, Sudbrook, every Thursday, consisting of concerts, penny readings, dissolving views, lectures, etc., and have afforded

Contractor's locomotive
(Source: Leicestershire Museums, Arts and Records Service)

much pleasure to the workmen and others, the charge for admission being only 1*d*. and 2*d*.

(*Chepstow Weekly Advertiser*, 2 February 1884)

Prominent in these affairs was the Severn Tunnel Glee Party, and the Severn Tunnel Cricket Club regularly gave concerts: A.O. Schenk, chief of Walker's engineering staff, was not only a very proficient cricketer, but reputedly a fine singer as well.

Incidents involving Severn Tunnel workers continued to be reported in the *Chepstow Weekly Adviser:*

Edward Thorpe, a Severn Tunnel employee, was charged with stealing a silk hankerchief valued at five shillings . . . the bench . . . discharged him. Thorpe was so elated with his discharge that he got gloriously drunk . . . he was brought up for being drunk and riotous . . . and was then sent to gaol for fourteen days in default of a fine.

(31 May 1884)

George Smith, a navvy, better known according to the custom of navvies by the nickname Monkey Tamer, was again brought up on a charge of stealing a piece of beef weighing about 24 lbs.

(12 July 1884)

John Johnson, a navvy, was charged with being drunk and disorderly at Chepstow on 3rd June . . . this was the third time the defendant had been before the magistrates within the last few months . . . defendant asked the Bench to give him a chance as it was very hot weather, and they let him

off with a fine of seven shillings and sixpence and eight
shillings costs.

(5 July 1884)

July saw nearly three miles of tunnel and well over a mile
of upper section of tunnel finished. The new pump was
installed at Five Miles Four Chains and the three new pumps
at Sudbrook were nearly ready for the final assault on the
Great Spring. Ballast was being laid along the bottom of the
tunnel in preparation for the railway tracks, and four steam
navvies had increased the rate of excavation on the Gloucestershire cutting: over 80,000 tons of material had been
removed in the last month alone.

In August 1884, the Institution of Mechanical Engineers
arrived for a tour of the works. Joe Talbot, who always acted
as guide on occasions such as this, was determined to give the
engineers an indication of what it was like to work underground. The miners were instructed to prepare and pack
about fifty holes with explosives in an unfinished section of
the tunnel. As soon as the visitors had filed past and reached a
point of safety, the fuses were lit and the miners made a hasty
retreat. The results were dramatic. Each of the fuses had been
cut to a different length and, as each charge exploded, the
report echoed and re-echoed along the finished sections of
tunnel, giving the impression of a continuous subterranean
bombardment, and startling all but the most experienced
engineers. The visitors were no doubt relieved to be hauled
back to the surface to clear the ringing from their ears.

By now, if work was to continue in the vicinity of the
Great Spring, the water would have to be diverted somehow.
Hawkshaw decided to drive another heading parallel to the

tunnel, but about 40 ft away, in order to intercept the Great Spring. The water could then be carried to the pumps, thus bypassing the unfinished area of tunnel.

The Great Spring originated from water which flowed through subterranean channels in the broken limestone and sandstone. It was thought that a great deal of water was also being lost underground through fissures in the bed of the Neddern, a little river which eventually joined the Severn. As a means of reducing the quantity of water that might reach the tunnel workings from this source, Hawkshaw instructed Walker to seal the bed of the river for a distance of 4 miles with over 7,000 tons of concrete.

By the end of September the new pumping power was ready and water was gradually released from behind the massive wall which held the Great Spring back. After three days of pumping it was possible to clamber through a small hole broken through the top of the headwall to inspect the heading beyond; it was still secure so work could now continue on the final 300 yd section of the tunnel between Sudbrook and Five Miles Four Chains.

The number of men employed on the works had risen steadily from 3–400 in 1882 to more than 3,500 in 1884. Foremen earned between 9*d.* and 10*d.* an hour; skilled labour (carpenters, miners, fitters, etc.), 5½*d.* to 8½*d.*; labourers 4*d.* to 5*d.*; and boys 2*d.* to 3½*d.* The average amount earned by a miner would be £1 18*s.* a week and a labourer £1 7*s.* 6*d.* a week. These wages were, by the standards of the time, very good; an agricultural labourer's wages in the 1880s would have been little more than 13*s.* a week. Work at the tunnel was therefore an attractive proposition to the unskilled male labour force of the region, especially to the men of the predominantly agricultural parishes of interior Monmouth.

On 17 October, Sir Daniel Gooch was a visitor to the works:

> I went this morning to the Severn Tunnel. Lord
> Besborough [a GWR director] met me there before lunch
> and we inspected the surface work and after lunch went
> below. It fortunately happened that the headings were just
> meeting and by the time we had finished lunch, the men
> had got a small hole through making the tunnel open
> throughout. I was the first to creep through and Lord
> Besborough followed me. It was a very difficult piece of
> navigation but by a little pulling in front and pushing
> behind we managed it and the men gave us some hearty
> cheers. I am glad I was the first to go through as I have
> great interest in this great work, which is now getting fast
> towards completion. . . . I hope by June or July next the
> tunnel will be finished. . . .

But in April 1885 an ominous report appeared in the local press:

> It has been persistently rumoured that water has of late
> found its way into the Severn Tunnel in such violence as to
> baffle the best efforts of the engineers, and to render
> necessary the abandonment of an undertaking that has been
> in hand for nearly
> 12 years. . . .

> (*Chepstow Weekly Advertiser*, 4 April 1885)

It was true that more water had been encountered as fissures connected with the Great Spring were struck. In fact the removal of virtually the last stone at the bottom of the tunnel had released a huge body of water. At another point

The fever hospital
(Source: John Harvey)

an 18 ft deep hole was revealed from which water boiled up
with such force that stones as big as a fist were thrown out.
But at no time were the works in danger; the immense
pumping power at Walker's disposal was more than a match
for these influxes. The report in the *Advertiser* continued:

> The contractor for the Severn Tunnel, Mr T.A. Walker,
> desires it to be known that there is no foundation whatever
> for such statements . . . so far as the contractor can see there
> is no reason whatever to doubt that by the end of June this
> stupendous undertaking may be practically finished.

At 8.00 a.m. on 18 April 1885, the last piece of brickwork
in the tunnel was completed. But much more grave matters
were occupying public attention; a serious smallpox outbreak
had occurred in the locality, and reports of deaths were
frequent. One bizarre incident was recounted in the local
newspaper:

> On Friday week a man, named Rawlings, in the employ of
> Mr T.A. Walker at the Severn Tunnel, died in the Infectious
> Hospital, which is built near the works, in the parish of
> Portskewett, of smallpox and the next day the body was
> buried in the parish graveyard. The widow and friends were
> desirous that the man should be interred in the adjoining
> parish of Caldecot, but the hospital authorities could not
> grant their wish as the disease had attacked the poor fellow
> in such a virulent form, and the body to be conveyed to
> Caldecot would have to be carried through a thickly
> populated district. On these grounds the authorities refused
> and the body was interred in the Portskewett graveyard.
> The relatives would not have this and the son at night with
> three others took a horse and cart to the place where the
> body was, dug it up and re-interred it at Caldecot, where he

The side heading, running parallel to the main tunnel, carrying the Great Spring to the pumps. The water is lifted nearly 170 ft to the surface to be discharged into the Severn. In this view the huge door at the Great Spring end of the passage, can be seen with the Great Spring itself in the foreground (Source: British Rail)

had already dug a grave. Last week the widow also became a victim to the fell disease and died. . . .

(*Chepstow Weekly Advertiser*, 2 May 1885)

In July, Hawkshaw was able to report that the work was nearing completion. The stone face marking the entrance to the tunnel had been built at the Welsh end, the English entrance was well in hand, and railway lines had been laid throughout the majority of the tunnel. The side heading now carried all the water from the Great Spring to the pumps through two pipes fitted with valves so that the water flow could be controlled. The intention was that the valves would be gradually closed, thus allowing the water to build up outside the tunnel; a gauge would measure the pressure.

6 An Improvident Opening

Diary of Sir Daniel Gooch, 5 September 1885:

> I took a special train today through the Severn Tunnel. We
> had a large party and all went off well. Mr Walker the
> contractor gave us a very liberal lunch at the works. This
> tunnel is a big work and has been a source of great anxiety
> to me. The large spring of water we cut on the Welsh side a
> short distance from the Severn has been a great cost and
> trouble.

The Illustrated London News reported the inaugural journey:

> Another great tunnel has become an accomplished fact; on
> 5th inst., forty passengers, including the chairman of the
> Great Western Railway (Sir Daniel Gooch), in five carriages
> drawn by a Great Western engine, 'showed the way'
> through the Severn Tunnel, which is four miles and a
> quarter long. The journey was done in eighteen minutes;
> but of course, it does not follow that such will be the usual
> rate. As the work was commenced in 1873, it may seem
> that everybody took plenty of time over it; but there were
> difficulties of many kinds not easy to explain in a small

space. The chief anxiety has been felt, no doubt, by Sir
Daniel Gooch, by Mr Richardson and Sir John Hawkshaw,
the engineer and consulting engineer, and, above all, by Mr
T.A. Walker, contractor; and they must be glad it is all over
– for the present.

(12 September 1885)

An account in *The Engineer* magazine describes the misgivings of some of the passengers on the inaugural journey:

The engineers were naturally confident in the soundness of
their work, but some of the passengers may be forgiven if
they experienced some slight trepidation on finding
themselves plunging into an unknown, way beneath the
widest and most stormy of English estuaries, then almost as
full as it could be, and with the knowledge that on several
occasions during construction both sea and springs had burst
through. The sensation of rushing through a land tunnel is
never pleasant, even to the oldest railway traveller, but it is
a much more trying ordeal to go slowly along a new track,
fully conscious that not far above one's head is the rolling
sea. When this journey comes to be done in ten minutes,
travellers will be glad to get over it, but it required all the
reassurances of the engineers to render the half hour's
passage bearable to the non-official members of the party,
more especially the ladies. Such natural uneasiness as existed
was likely to be increased by the circumstance that the
tunnel was in darkness, the Brush electric lights in use
during the execution having to be removed to give room for
the train. The carriages were, of course, brilliantly lighted;
but so far as the tunnel was concerned, it was a veritable *de
profundis*. The ground through which the bore had been
made is largely sandstone, coal, and fairly solid substances;
but the pioneer passengers were not much alive to that
circumstance. Doubts and misgivings gradually vanished

when it was found that not only was there no sound or sign
of the treacherous ocean; but with the exception of a slight
leakage near where a powerful spring broke through two
years ago, this subaqueous roadway was as dry as the driest
land subway. Moreover, owing to the powerful fan kept
vigorously working, the atmosphere was beautifully clear,
and the daylight at one end of the tunnel could be seen like
a brilliant star, nearly two miles away.

On 7 September 1885, Walker, who was by now feeling
the strain of the tunnel works, set sail from Southampton to
Buenos Aires to complete estimates for some dock works on
the River Plate, confident that the tunnel would be all right.
But on 30 October 1885 he received a telegram from
Hawkshaw asking him to return to England immediately.
The valves in the side heading were now fully closed and the
pressure of water on the tunnel brickwork was steadily
growing. Bricks in the lining had started to break, pieces flew
off with a loud report, and jets of water began to shoot across
the tunnel. Hawkshaw had determined that the lining should
be constructed as 'rings', six successive layers of brickwork
to build up the required thickness. But in some parts of the
tunnel, water found a way between the layers, forcing them
apart, first the inner layer or ring, then the second, and so on.
The most dramatic effect of the water pressure was seen on
the bottom or invert of the tunnel. An area of about 40 square
yards of brickwork slowly rose under the pressure, then
collapsed in a heap, allowing the water to run away. After the
loose bricks had been cleared, the second layer of brickwork
rose and failed in a similar way, and then the third began to
rise. On his return from South America, Walker headed
straight to the works to confront the latest crisis. If the whole
of this section of tunnel lining were not to be destroyed, the

Another view of the side heading which runs parallel to the main tunnel. In the foreground is a massive wall about 9 ft thick, with two valves and a passage; the source of the Great Spring is in the distance (Source: **British Rail**)

water pressure would have to be reduced. He ordered the valves to be opened to allow the water to run away to the pumps.

Richardson had originally specified 'vertical bond' for the brickwork, in which the full thickness of the wall would be built of bricks which interlocked with one another, thus preventing the layers from separating. Hawkshaw rejected this proposal on the grounds that it would be too expensive, since a wall built like this would need special bricks. Richardson countered this argument by contending that a lining built his way would only have needed to be 18 in thick, whereas Hawkshaw's method required 30 in, at the same time acknowledging that the massive water pressure would still cause leakage between the joints. At the end of the project the brick lining would represent more than half the cost of the tunnel.

Sir Daniel Gooch agreed with Richardson. He felt that Richardson had not been given sufficient credit for the tunnel and went on to say:

> In carrying out the Works, two mistakes were made, both of which were objected to by Richardson. One was the deepening of the tunnel to get more cover over the Shoots by 20 feet. The construction of the Work showed this was the soundest part of the tunnel, and had been proved so by the heading being in solid pennant rock, and did not require the extra thickness overhead. But the consequence of this deepening was the striking of the Big Spring. The other mistake was lining the tunnel in half brick rings.

For some years Richardson had been discussing the possibility of Bristol Waterworks Company using the water from the Great Spring by carrying it under the Severn through a heading running parallel to the tunnel. The proposal was that the waterworks should build the necessary shafts and heading and that the Great Western Railway would charge them for the pumping of the water. In a letter to Sir Daniel Gooch, dated 14 December 1885, Richardson discussed the latest problems with the tunnel, adding: '. . . if the Water Company get access to the Spring, as I think they are inclined to do, they will save the Railway Company just so much.'

It was becoming clear that the tunnel lining would never be capable of resisting the huge pressures created by the Great Spring. To make matters worse, Bristol Waterworks decided against using the spring water. There was only one option left; the waters of the Great Spring would have to be pumped permanently. Hawkshaw directed Walker to construct another brick lined shaft 180 ft deep with an internal diameter of 29 ft, adjacent to the side heading which carried the spring water. A huge pumphouse with a floor area substantially bigger than a tennis court and 60 ft high would be built over the shaft to house six big Cornish beam engines, each with a colossal wrought-iron beam 35 ft long to power the pumps. The resulting pumping power would be phenomenal; in just one hour the pumps would be capable of emptying the equivalent of about eight large modern swimming pools, amounting to well over 25 million gallons a day. The engines would be driven by steam from twelve big boilers in an adjacent building.

At the end of December 1885 an order went to Harveys of Hayle for the six massive pumping engines, together with four more for other shafts, and all the necessary boilers, pumps and associated equipment, with a request to give the order priority over all other work and to deliver promptly. It was fortuitous that the order went to the foundry at this time;

Exterior view of the permanent pumphouse at Sudbrook
(Source: British Rail)

work was running down alarmingly due to the collapse of the Cornish mining industry. The company would supply workmen, under the direction of Francis Harvey, for the erection of the engines and pumps in the new engine house which was to be built by Walker's men. But there were delays in deliveries (the Great Western were usually the defaulters) and incomplete assignments; and Francis Harvey found it difficult to work with Walker, who was apt to treat him as subordinate, even though the erection of the machinery was a major part of the work.

Sir Daniel Gooch remained optimistic, but clearly he had been feeling the strain, as his diary shows:

> A coal train was worked through the Severn Tunnel today from Newport and Cardiff to Bristol and on to Southampton. All went well, and I hope to open for goods and coal on 1st March. This has been a very anxious work for me, we have had so many serious difficulties. One has felt a doubt whether we ought to persevere with so large an expenditure, but I never lost hope of succeeding in the end.

> (Saturday 9 January 1886)

The task of constructing the permanent pumping arrangements was tackled with great energy by Walker and his men; the new shaft (to be known as No. 1) and engine house were commenced in February 1886. The shaft, equivalent in depth to an eighteen-storey building, and substantially larger in diameter than the finished tunnel, was blasted downwards from ground level and upwards from the tunnel below in record time: eight weeks and three days. Within another eight weeks, the 3 ft thick brick lining was finished – a remarkable achievement.

The six massive Cornish beam engines in the permanent pumphouse, Sudbrook
(Source: City of Bristol Museum & Art Gallery)

Sir John Hawkshaw was bent on completing the work so that the tunnel could be opened by Christmas 1886. One day in July 1886 the domineering consulting engineer arrived at Sudbrook to express himself dissatisfied with progress in the erection of the engines and pumps. At the time, Harvey's men were working a long day shift, but it was Hawkshaw who sent a terse message to the Hayle works:

> I wired you this morning to the following effect: 'You must instruct Rowe to work night and day immediately'. And now I write to confirm this.

Rowe was Francis Harvey's foreman at Sudbrook. Harvey was a very competent engineer; quite why Hawkshaw should ignore him in his directive is a mystery. Harvey acquiesced to Hawkshaw's demands and ordered his men to work day and night with a view to getting the first two engines working by the end of the month. But there would be problems for him from an unexpected source:

> Saturday July 24th 1886: We are getting on well with the work and all the men are working hard. I am afraid we shall have to work tomorrow but I do not quite know how Walker will like it, as last Sunday he said he should not allow us to do so again, but I presume we are working for the Great Western Railway and not Mr Walker.

> Sunday July 25th 1886: Mr Walker came out just now in a terrible rage and stopped our working, and threatened if we did not stop to turn us out by force. I hear he left the pulpit in order to stop us. We are in rather a peculiar position here, as we have in a way to work for the GWR and at the same time to depend on him for any little thing in the way of stores we may require, also to use his forge; so that we are

The replacement ventilation fan for the Severn Tunnel, 27 ft in diameter. The original, fitted in 1886, was even bigger – 40 ft in diameter
(Source: *GWR Magazine*)

obliged to put up with a lot of nonsense. But at the same time I think he ought to know that he has no right to interfere with us in any way.

This incident probably explains why Harveys were given so little credit by Walker in his subsequent account of the construction of the tunnel. From the early days, and throughout the course of the works, everything depended upon keeping the tunnel dry; this could not have been done without the machinery and expertise provided by Harveys. Notwithstanding this setback, Francis Harvey and his men had two engines ready to work by the end of July, and two more were ready by the end of October. Walker's men had lined the side heading with brickwork to carry the waters of the Great Spring to the new shaft, and by the end of August permanent ventilation for the tunnel had been provided in the shape of a massive fan, 40 ft in diameter and 12 ft wide, housed in a specially designed building adjacent to the new pumphouse.

The diary of Sir Daniel Gooch, September 1886:

We opened our Severn Tunnel on the 1st for goods traffic. The first train that passed through was a goods leaving Bristol at 6.35 p.m. Fourteen trains were worked through during the night, and all was most satisfactory. This has been a long and very anxious and costly job. Our estimate for it was about £900,000. We have now spent over £1,600,000. The water is still a large expense to us but it is under perfect control.

Sir Daniel Gooch resolved to open the tunnel in December 1886 for the Christmas passenger traffic between Bristol and South Wales, but this would need to be sanctioned by a government inspector. Colonel Rich inspected the works and, as part of his report, pronounced that: 'The works appear to be very good and substantial, and to have been carried out with great care and judgement' (22 November 1886).

Accordingly, the tunnel was finally opened for traffic on 1 December 1886, nearly fourteen years from the time the Great Western Railway had started the work and nearly seven years from the time Thomas Walker had taken charge:

> Without fuss or demonstration of any kind the first passenger trains passed through the gigantic tube linking the shores of Monmouthshire and Gloucestershire on Wednesday morning. The first train left the terminus, Temple Meads Bristol, at 6.15 a.m. and conveyed between seventy and eighty passengers through the tunnel. Many of the leading officials of the Great Western Railway Company accompanied the train. The train, which was of an ordinary character, and carried a fair amount of luggage, was despatched with the usual formalities and not a single cheer was raised and not the slightest demonstration was made as it steamed out of the station punctually to the time notified in the timetables.
>
> The journey under the Severn occupied nine minutes twenty seconds and when the train emerged from the Rogiet end, many of the passengers gave a hearty and vigorous cheer, which was enthusiastically taken up by a number of persons who had congregated on the crest of the deep cutting through which the line runs to the junction with the railway on the Monmouthshire side of the river. It was observed that the ivy clad tower of the Rogiet church was adorned with a Union Jack, but this was the only display of bunting along the whole route.
>
> As the first tinge of colour became visible in the clouds overhead, some dozen or more passengers took their seats in

The permanent pumphouse at Five Miles Four Chains. The outer ends of the two engine beams can be clearly seen
(Source: British Rail/OPC)

*The Gloucestershire tunnel mouth at about the time of the opening in
December 1886
(Source: British Rail)*

the 6.45 train from Cardiff bound for Bristol via the tunnel and within a couple of minutes were speeding on their way. As far as outward appearance went, and Cardiff was concerned, a stranger would have thought there was nothing out of the ordinary in the event, so little interest was manifested. But at Newport, and more especially at Little Magor, it was apparent something more than common was going on, and freight was increased considerably, many of the new passengers evidently 'going for the sake of the run'. With scarce a wait at either place however 'underground railway' time was kept. The train was again rolling along at a splendid speed and before those on board quite knew where they were, a shrill whistle, a sudden darkening, for it was now nearly broad daylight, and 'we are in' told them they were in, and rushing down a clearly perceptible decline towards a point a hundred feet below the bed of the broad estuary. In a trice watches were out and the windows down, the first to keep time, the other to test the ventilation. The inrush of icy cold air as clear and pure as if the trip across was being made in the old way, over, instead of under the channel, showed the latter was alright. The ventilation indeed was simply superb. All passengers by rail have suffered, and suffer the inconveniences incident to a tunnel, but with a freedom from smell truly marvellous and an entire absence of reverberation or oscillation, the submarine journey, if such it may be called, proved to be more like a run through a pretty deep cutting than through a tunnel four and a quarter miles long.

For about three minutes and a half after entering there was no mistaking the fact that a sharp gradient was being descended, then, a momentary rumble as the train passed over the curve of the arc, for the tube dips in the centre, and then the locomotive at an ever decreasing speed climbed the opposite gradient to emerge once more into daylight.

(*Chepstow Weekly Advertiser*, Saturday
4 December 1886)

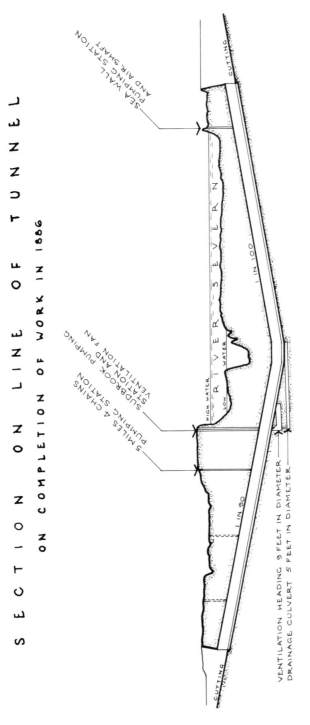

Section on line of tunnel on completion of work in 1886
(Source: author)

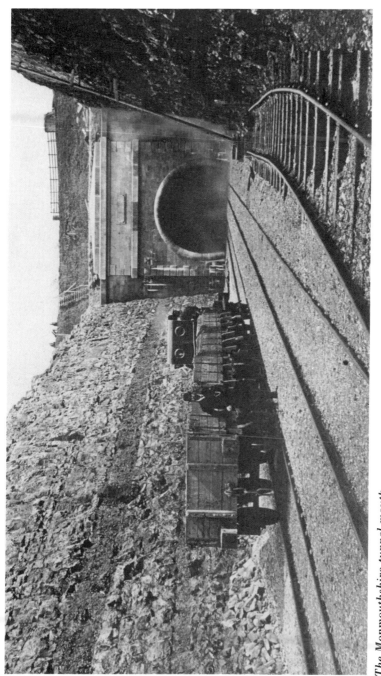

The Monmouthshire tunnel mouth
(Source: John Harvey)

Within six years of the opening of the tunnel, most of the protagonists would be dead: Hawkshaw aged eighty, Gooch aged seventy-three, Lambert aged fifty-five and Walker aged 61, the latter dying at Mount Ballan, the house where he lived close to the project which had occupied him for seven years of his life. Richardson would live until 1896. But the tunnel survives to this day, a lasting tribute to their determination and energy and the massive workforce that changed ideas into reality. The immaculate steam engines and pumps would continue their vital work of keeping the tunnel dry, devouring one and a half trainloads of coal a day, until the beginning of the 1960s, when the massive beams finally came to rest, the responsibility being handed over to electric pumps.

On a foggy night in October 1960, two tankers in the Severn estuary became locked together after a collision and were swept by the fast tide into a pier of the Severn bridge in a mass of flames. Two huge sections of the bridge toppled into the estuary. It was never rebuilt, its long but less than illustrious career ending in ignominy in 1970 when the last of the bridge skeleton disappeared under the hand of the demolition contractor.

Sudbrook, numbering among its inhabitants many descendants of the tunnel workers, remains recognizable as the village created by Thomas Walker. Still to be seen are the big pumphouses, and the large houses with their long dormitory-like bedrooms, built originally for two married couples and the twelve or more lodgers who slept in shifts after returning from their exertions in the tunnel below:

One such experience as the Severn Tunnel, with its ever-varying and strangely contorted strata, and the dangers from floods above and floods below, has been sufficient for me. One sub-aqueous tunnel is quite enough for a lifetime.

(Thomas Walker)

Selected References

Public Records Office, Kew:

Rail 250/17–37	GWR meeting minutes 1860 to 1886.
Rail 253/128	Severn Tunnel and bridge; correspondence and reports.
Rail 257/1	Correspondence, Gooch/Richardson, Hawkshaw et al. 1867–88.
Rail 257/2	Reports, tenders and estimates 1874–87.
Rail 265/13,14,15	GWR report on Severn Tunnel 1885.
Rail 775/2	Hawkshaw/Gooch; GWR directors' letters.
Rail 775/3	Richardson/Gooch; GWR directors' letters.
Rail 775/12	Tunnel drawings.
Rail 775/19	Shaft contract 1873.
Rail 1008/21	Richardson/Gooch letter.
Rail 1014/2,13	Proposal for bridge over Severn (1846).
Rail 1014/32	Severn Bridge Railway.
Rail 1057/2955	Fowler's Line.
ZLIB 1/14B	Diaries of Sir Daniel Gooch.
ZLIB 9	T.A. Walker paper 1887 (see below).

County Record Office, Gloucester:

Q/RUm　　　　　　　Plans for Severn crossings.

Books and technical papers:

Blower, A.　　　　　　*British Railways Tunnels*, Ian Allen, 1964.

Booker, F.　　　　　　*The Great Western Railway*, David & Charles, 1977.

Brooke, D.　　　　　　'The Railway Navvy of the 1881 census', in *Quarterly Journal of Social Affairs*, 1986, 2, (4) 363–377.

Brooke, D.　　　　　　'The Railway Navvy – A reassessment' (Draft paper – University of Bath).

Buchanan, A., and Cossons, N.　　　*The Industrial Archaeology of the Bristol Region*, David & Charles, 1969.

Buchanan, A. and Williams, M.　　　*Brunel's Bristol.*

Coleman, T.　　　　　*The Railway Navvies*, Hutchinson, 1972.

Davis, Sir R.　　　　　*A few recollections of an old Lambeth factory*, Siebe Gorman & Co. Ltd.

Davis, Sir R.　　　　　*Breathing in irrespirable atmospheres*, Siebe Gorman & Co. Ltd. (Pub Catherine Press Ltd) 1946.

Davis, Sir R.　　　　　*Deep Diving and Submarine Operations*, Siebe Gorman Diving Manual.

Dugan, J.　　　　　　*Man explores the sea*, Hamish Hamilton, 1957.

Huxley, R.　　　　　　*The rise and fall of the Severn Bridge Railway 1872–1970*, Alan Sutton, 1984.

Joby, R.S.	*The railway builders – Lives and works of the Victorian railway contractors*, David & Charles, 1983.
Jordan, S.	*Severn Enterprise*, Arthur H. Stockwell, 1977.
MacDermot, E.T., and Clinker, C.R.	*History of the Great Western Railway*, Vol. 2, Ian Allen, 1964.
Marshall, J.	*A biographical dictionary of railway engineers*, David & Charles, 1978.
Richardson, C.	'The Severn Tunnel', *Bristol Naturalist Society Proceedings,* Vol. 5, 1888.
Richardson, C.	'The Severn Tunnel; Its origin and construction', Paper: September 1888.
Sandstrom, G.E.	*The History of Tunnelling*, Barrie & Rockcliffe, 1963.
Schenk, A.O.	'The construction of the Severn Tunnel'. Paper: 1912. South Wales Institute of Engineers. Proceedings, Vol. 28, No. 4.
Sullivan, R.	*Navvyman*, Coracle Books, 1983.
Vale, E.	*The Harveys of Hayle*, Barton, Truro, 1966.
Vincent, M.	*Lines to Avonmouth*, Oxford Pub. Co., 1979
Walker, T.A.	'The Severn Tunnel': paper read at British Association, Manchester, 1887.
Walker, T.A.	*The Severn Tunnel – Its construction and difficulties*, Bentley, London, 1888, Reprinted by Kingsmead reprints, Bath, 1969.
Williams, D.H.	*Sudbrook Village.*

Wilson, R.B.   *Sir Daniel Gooch – Memoirs and Diary*, David & Charles, 1969.

Newspapers, periodicals and other sources

Barry and Cadoxton Journal: Supplement; 6 December 1889.
Chepstow Weekly Advertiser: dates noted in text.
The Engineer: 20 January 1865: 'Railway under the Severn'
20 January 1865: 'The high level bridge across the Severn'
20 January 1865: 'The rival Severn schemes'
10 March 1865: 'The high level bridge over the Severn'
11 September 1885: 'Opening of the Severn Tunnel'

Engineering: 21 January 1870
5 May 1871
4 August 1871
29 September 1871
3 November 1871
24 November 1871
1 December 1871
22 December 1871
29 December 1871
23 February 1872
3 May 1872
6 September 1872
8 November 1872
15 November 1872
28 March 1873

25 April 1873

 1 August 1873

24 October 1873

10 September 1875: 'The Severn Tunnel'; Charles Richardson

15 October 1875

17 December 1875

24 October 1879: 'The Severn Railway Bridge'

29 August 1884: 'The Severn Tunnel Railway'; J. Clark Hawkshaw

27 August 1886: 'The Severn Tunnel'

Engineering Wonders of the World – Part 2; ed., Archibald Williams – Thomas Nelson & Sons, 1909.

Great Western Railway Magazine: 1889; Series of articles; 'The Severn Tunnel' Charles Richardson January 1890; p. 25, 'The Severn Tunnel' Charles Richardson March 1924; Vol. 36, 'The Severn Tunnel ventilating plant' Warren.

The Illustrated London News: 5 September 1963; 'The Bristol and South Wales Union Railway'. 25 October 1879; 'The new railway bridge over the Severn, at Lydney, Gloucestershire', 12 September 1885; p. 260.

Journal of the Gwent Local History Council: Vol. 4, No. 45, p. 27.

Proceedings of the Institution of Civil Engineers: Vol. 72, 116 and 121.

The Times; dates noted in text.

Western Daily Press; dates noted in text.

Brunel letters; Tyndall Avenue Library, Bristol University.

D